THE REMARKABLE
SINE FUNCTIONS

THE REMARKABLE
SINE FUNCTIONS

BY

A. I. MARKUSHEVICH
Moscow State University

Translated by Scripta Technica, Inc.

Translation Editor: Leon Ehrenpreis
Courant Institute of Mathematical Sciences
New York University

NEW YORK

AMERICAN ELSEVIER PUBLISHING COMPANY INC.

1966

Originally published as
ZAMECHATEL'NYYE SINUSY
Nauka Press, Moscow, 1965

SOLE DISTRIBUTORS FOR GREAT BRITAIN
ELSEVIER PUBLISHING COMPANY, LTD.
Barking, Essex, England

SOLE DISTRIBUTORS FOR THE CONTINENT OF EUROPE
ELSEVIER PUBLISHING COMPANY
Amsterdam, The Netherlands

Library of Congress Catalog Card Number: 66-29781

ANNOTATION _____

The present book represents an attempt at uniform consideration of the various sines (the circular and hyperbolic sines, the lemniscate sine, and the sine amplitude of Jacobi) as special cases of the so-called generalized sine—all of them functions defined as the inverse of some integral. It requires a certain amount of mathematical training and is intended for sufficiently prepared readers who have mastered mathematical analysis as taught in university courses.

CONTENTS

Of the functions studied in elementary mathematics, the trigonometric functions stand out by virtue of their geometrical definition. Without stopping for inconsequential variations of the same idea, we may say that the sine and cosine are introduced as coordinates of a point on the unit circle. The independent variable is treated as an angle or arc of a circle.

In the present book, we shall show how it is possible, by beginning with other curves (such as the equilateral hyperbola or Bernoulli's lemniscate (a curve having the form of a figure-eight), to define interesting and important functions analogous to the trigonometric functions, similar to them in some respects but possessing certain new characteristics. These functions are called respectively *hyperbolic* and *lemniscate* functions. In analogy with them, we shall refer to the trigonometric functions as *circular* functions.

We shall consider all these functions as special cases of the *generalized sine,* that is, the function inverse to the function defined by an integral of the form

$$x = \int\limits_0^y \frac{dz}{\sqrt{1 + mz^2 + nz^4}}.$$

Here, the circular sine corresponds to the case $m = -1$, $n = 0$; the hyperbolic sine corresponds to the case $m = 1$, $n = 0$; the lemniscate sine corresponds to the case $m = 0$, $n = -1$. If $m = -1 - k^2$ and $n = k^2$ (for $0 < k < 1$), we obtain for the function inverse to that defined by the integral the so-called *sine amplitude* of Jacobi. The problem of the pendulum leads to a study of this last function.

To study the properties of all these functions in a uniform way, we need first of all to define them as functions of a complex variable and then establish an addition theorem for them. This path was already taken at the end of the eighteenth century by the young Gauss in his *Tagebuch*.

The reader is assumed to have a familiarity with the elements of analytic geometry and differential and integral calculus. The necessary material on integration in the complex plane will be given in the present book though proofs will be omitted.

The ultimate purpose of the book is to acquaint the reader not possessing an extensive knowledge of the theory of functions of a complex variable with the simplest representatives of the class of elliptic functions, namely, lemniscate functions and the somewhat more general Jacobian elliptic functions.

In conclusion, we warn the reader that this book is not intended for light reading. He must read it with his pencil in his hand.

The Author

_____

CHAPTER 1

Geometric Definition of Circular, Hyperbolic, and Lemniscate Functions

1. The circular functions are defined and their properties are discussed in high-school mathematics classes. Here, we shall briefly expound familiar facts in a form that will be convenient for us to bring out the similarities and dissimilarities sharply.

Let us begin with the unit circle

$$x^2 + y^2 = 1. \tag{1}$$

The arc length from the point C to a point A (see Fig. 1) is defined up to an integral multiple of the total circumference of the circle, namely, $2\pi k$. Here, k is the number of complete revolutions about the coordinate origin described by a point on

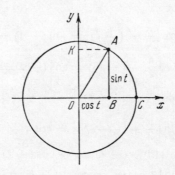

FIG. 1.

the circle as it moves from C to A. We take the counter-clockwise direction as positive.

The coordinates x and y of the point A are independent of the number of complete revolutions made. Therefore, they are periodic functions of t with period 2π. By definition,

$$x = \cos t, \quad y = \sin t. \tag{2}$$

From this it follows that, for arbitrary t,

$$\cos^2 t + \sin^2 t = 1. \tag{3}$$

It follows from the symmetry of the circle about the x-axis that

$$\cos(-t) = \cos t, \quad \sin(-t) = -\sin t. \tag{4}$$

If we also use the symmetry about the bisector of the first and third quadrants (by virtue of which the abscissa and ordinate of any point on the unit circle are interchanged), we see that

$$\cos\left(\frac{\pi}{2} - t\right) = \sin t, \quad \sin\left(\frac{\pi}{2} - t\right) = \cos t. \tag{5}$$

Each of the formulas (5) enables us to obtain a definition of either of these two functions in terms of the other; for example, we can define $\cos t$ in terms of $\sin t$ (assumed already defined).

As consequences of formulas (4) and (5), we can derive all the simple "reduction" formulas. Thus, for example, we obtain the following pairs of formulas; the derivation of each pair after the first uses the preceding formulas:

$$\cos\left(\frac{\pi}{2} + t\right) = \cos\left[\frac{\pi}{2} - (-t)\right] = \sin(-t) = -\sin t,$$

$$\sin\left(\frac{\pi}{2} + t\right) = \sin\left[\frac{\pi}{2} - (-t)\right] = \cos(-t) = \cos t;$$

$$\cos(\pi - t) = \cos\left[\frac{\pi}{2} + \left(\frac{\pi}{2} - t\right)\right] = -\sin\left(\frac{\pi}{2} - t\right) = -\cos t,$$

$$\sin(\pi - t) = \sin\left[\frac{\pi}{2} + \left(\frac{\pi}{2} - t\right)\right] = \cos\left(\frac{\pi}{2} - t\right) = \sin t;$$

$$\cos(\pi + t) = \cos[\pi - (-t)] = -\cos(-t) = -\cos t,$$

$$\sin(\pi + t) = \sin[\pi - (-t)] = \sin(-t) = -\sin t;$$

$$\cos(2\pi + t) = \cos[\pi + (\pi + t)] = -\cos(\pi + t) = \cos t,$$

$$\sin(2\pi + t) = \sin[\pi + (\pi + t)] = -\sin(\pi + t) = \sin t.$$

We note that the second pair of formulas can be derived immediately from the symmetry of the circle about the y-axis and that the third can be derived from the symmetry about the coordinate origin. The fourth pair expresses the periodicity, mentioned above, of the circular functions.

Defintion (2) and equation (1) enable us to answer the question regarding the number and nature of the solution of equations of the form

$$\sin t = \alpha \text{ or } \cos t = \alpha,$$

where α is a real number.

For example, consider the equation

$$\sin t = \alpha. \tag{6}$$

We may assert that, for $|\alpha| > 1$, this equation has no solution at all. For $|\alpha| \leqslant 1$, there exists at least one solution in the interval $0 \leqslant t < 2\pi$. Specifically,

if $\alpha = 1$, the only solution is $t = \dfrac{\pi}{2}$;

if $0 < \alpha < 1$, there are two solutions t_1 and t_2;
furthermore, $0 < t_1 < \dfrac{\pi}{2}$ and $\dfrac{\pi}{2} < t_2 = \pi - t_1 < \pi$;

if $\alpha = 0$, there are two solutions, namely, $t_1 = 0$ and $t_2 = \pi$;

if $-1 < \alpha < 0$, there are two solutions t_1 and t_2;
furthermore, $\pi < t_1 < \dfrac{3\pi}{2}$ and $\dfrac{3\pi}{2} < t_2 = 3\pi - t_1 < 2\pi$;

if $\alpha = -1$, there is only the solution $t = \dfrac{3\pi}{2}$.

Of course, in the cases of α equal to 1 or -1, we can speak of two solutions that coincide. If $t_1 \neq t_2$, the corresponding values of the cosine are negatives of each other:

$$\cos t_1 = - \cos t_2.$$

Geometrically, solution of equation (6) reduces to finding points on the circle (1) of given ordinate $y = \alpha$ and the evaluation of the lengths of the arcs terminating at the points found (see Fig. 2).

All that has been said in the present section is well illustrated on the graphs of $\sin t$ and $\cos t$. The construction of these graphs depends somewhat on the definitions accepted (see Fig. 3).

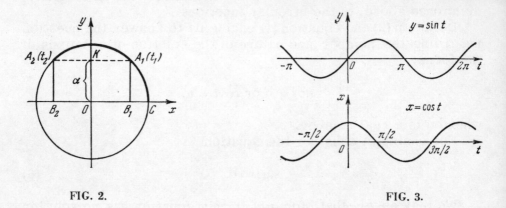

FIG. 2.   FIG. 3.

We note that we might interpret the parameter t in the definition (2) geometrically not only as the arc length CA but also as twice the area of the sector OCA:

$$t = 2 \text{ area } OCA. \tag{7}$$

Here, we need to regard the sector as produced by a moving radius displaced from the position OC to the position OA. If the radius undergoes k complete rotations in the process (where k can be either negative or positive (according to the direction of the rotation), the area swept by it will be equal to $k\pi$. Thus, we have the term $2k\pi$ in the definition of t given by formula (7).

2. Now, instead of the unit circle, let us consider the unit equilateral hyperbola

$$x^2 - y^2 = 1. \tag{8}$$

Equations (1) and (8) resemble each other much more than do the curves representing them (cf. Figs. 1 and 4). In fact, this is putting it mildly. Equations (1) and (8) differ from each other only by the sign in front of y^2. On the other hand, the curves shown in Figures 1 and 4 are not the least bit like each other. Yet, it is the equations that we must trust rather than our eyes. The similarity in the equations entails a far-reaching similarity in the properties of the curves, which we discover when we compare the circular with the hyperbolic functions.

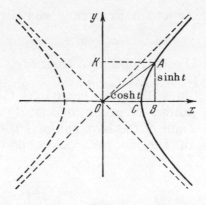

FIG. 4.

Let us denote by t twice the area of the sector OCA:

$$t = 2 \text{ area } OCA;$$

We shall consider the area of OCA positive if the rotation from OC to OA is carried out in the counterclockwise direction and we shall consider it negative in the opposite case. If the point A describes the right branch of the hyperbola shown in **Fig. 4** as y increases from $-\infty$ to $+\infty$, then t increases also from $-\infty$ to $+\infty$. The coordinates x and y of the point A can be regarded as single-valued functions of t. We define

$$x = \cosh t, \quad y = \sinh t. \tag{9}$$

Here, the abbreviations "cosh" and "sinh" are for the expressions *consinus hyperbolicus* (hyperbolic cosine) and *sinus hyperbolicus* (hyperbolic sine).

It follows from the definition that, for arbitrary t,

$$\cosh^2 t - \sinh^2 t = 1. \tag{10}$$

Using the symmetry of a hyperbola about the x-axis, we conclude that

$$\cosh(-t) = \cosh t, \quad \sinh(-t) = -\sinh t \tag{11}$$

(cf. the graphs of $\cosh t$ and $\sinh t$ in Fig. 5).

The equation

$$\sinh(t) = \alpha \tag{12}$$

has one and only one root for arbitrary real α. The equation

$$\cosh t = \alpha \qquad (13)$$

has no root at all if $\alpha < 1$, one root (namely, $t = 0$) if $\alpha = 1$, and two roots t_1 and t_2 $(= -t_1)$ if $\alpha > 1$.

Geometrically, the solution of equations (12) and (13) can be reduced to finding points of given ordinate y or given abscissa $x \geqslant 1$ on the right branch of the hyperbola (10) and to the evaluation of the areas of the sectors corresponding to the points found (Fig. 6).

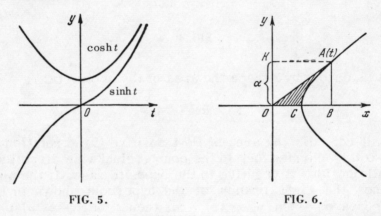

FIG. 5.   FIG. 6.

3. Before defining the lemniscate functions, we note that it is possible to give to the circular functions a geometric interpretation different from the interpretation given in section 1. Specifically, let us look at the circle of unit diameter tangent to the x-axis at the origin and lying in the upper half-plane: $x^2 + y^2 - y = 0$ (see Fig. 7). Obviously, the chord OA connecting

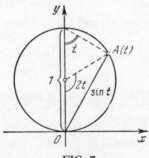

FIG. 7.

the end points of the arc OA of length t is equal to $\sin t$. Therefore, it would be possible to construct the theory of circular functions by defining

$$\sin t = OA, \quad t = \text{length } \overset{\frown}{OA}. \tag{14}$$

It follows from this definition that $\sin t$ increases from 0 to 1 as t increases from 0 to $\pi/2$. As t increases beyond $\pi/2$, the sine decreases and vanishes as $t = \pi$. (Under the conditions stated, π is the circumference of the circle.)

Let us complete our definition by agreeing that $\sin t$ changes sign every time that it passes through the value 0 as t increases. Then, we need to take the length of OA in formula (14) with the minus sign for $\pi < t < 2\pi$ and with the plus sign for $2\pi < t < 3\pi$, etc. Only under such a supplementary convention will our new definition coincide with the preceding one, and only then, in particular, will the period of the sine be 2π (rather than π as would be the case if we considered the length of the chord OA positive for all possible values of the arc OA, which would then differ by integral multiples of π).

The second circular function, the cosine, is defined in terms of the sine by the equation

$$\cos t = \sin\left(\frac{\pi}{2} - t\right). \tag{15}$$

4. Let us look at Bernoulli's lemniscate shown in Fig. 8. This is the curve consisting of all points in the plane such that the product of their distances from two given points, called the *foci* of the lemniscate, is constant. In the present case, the points $(1/2, 1/2)$ and $(-1/2, -1/2)$ are chosen as the foci and the constant distance product is $1/2$. Therefore, the equation of the lemniscate is of the form

$$\sqrt{\left(x - \frac{1}{2}\right)^2 + \left(y - \frac{1}{2}\right)^2} \cdot \sqrt{\left(x + \frac{1}{2}\right)^2 + \left(y + \frac{1}{2}\right)^2} = \frac{1}{2},$$

or, after squaring both sides and simplifying,

$$(x^2 + y^2)^2 - 2xy = 0. \tag{16}$$

Thus, Bernoulli's lemniscate is a fourth-order algebraic curve.

Let us introduce polar coordinates r and φ, taking the x-axis as the polar axis. Then,

$$x = r\cos\varphi, \quad y = r\sin\varphi.$$

Thus, the equation of the lemniscate in polar coordinates becomes

$$r^2 = \sin 2\varphi. \tag{17}$$

The variable r attains its maximum value, namely, 1 at $\varphi = \pi/4$.

It follows from equation (17) (or (16)) that the lemniscate is symmetric about the coordinate origin. Furthermore, it is symmetric about each of the diagonal lines bisecting the angles between the coordinate axes: if $x = a$ and $y = b$ satisfy equation (16), so do the pairs $(-a, -b)$, (b, a), and $(-b, -a)$.

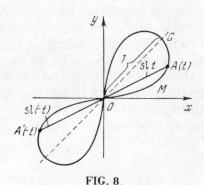

FIG. 8.

5. Suppose that a movable point M starts at the origin and moves in such a way as to describe that portion of the lemniscate lying in the first quadrant, moving in the positive (i.e., counterclockwise) direction. Since it is being displaced along an arc tangent to the y-axis when it first returns to the origin, it is natural to require that it be moving along an arc tangent to that axis as it enters the next (third) quadrant in the course of its motion. Accordingly, we must take the clockwise direction for the positive direction of motion of the point as it moves around that portion of the lemniscate in the third quadrant. When the point is finishing its first complete trip over the entire lemniscate and is beginning a new one, the point leaves the third and enters the first quadrant along an arc tangent to the x-axis. The motion thus described is then repeated.

Let us denote the length of the entire lemniscate by 2ω. Thus, the length of the arc OMC is equal to $\omega/2$. Just as in the case of a circle, we shall assume that the variable point M moves from an initial point O of the arc to its terminal point A after some number of complete courses over the entire lemniscate in either the positive or the negative direction. Thus, the length t of an arbitrary arc OA is determined only up to an integral multiple of 2ω. Therefore, r, the length of the chord OA, is a periodic function of t with period 2ω.

We complete the definition of this function by agreeing that it changes sign every time it passes through the origin with continuous increase in t.

In analogy with the circular sine, we shall refer to the function that we have just defined for all real values of t as the *lemniscate sine* and we shall denote it as follows:

$$OA = r = \operatorname{sl} t. \tag{18}$$

Here, the letters "sl" are the initials of the expression *sinus lemniscaticus*. We note in particular that

$$\operatorname{sl} \frac{\omega}{2} = 1. \tag{18'}$$

From the symmetry of the lemniscate about the origin and the convention adopted regarding sign, it follows that $\operatorname{sl} t$ is an odd function (see Fig. 8):

$$\operatorname{sl}(-t) = -\operatorname{sl} t. \tag{19}$$

From the symmetry about the bisector of the first and third quadrants, we have (see Fig. 9)

$$\operatorname{sl}(\omega - t) = \operatorname{sl} t. \tag{20}$$

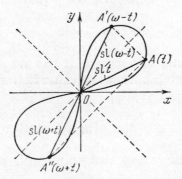

FIG. 9.

Analogously, from the symmetry about the bisector of the second and fourth quadrants, we have (see Fig. 9)

$$\operatorname{sl}(\omega + t) = -\operatorname{sl} t. \tag{21}$$

Actually, (21) is a simple consequence of equations (19) and (20):

$$\operatorname{sl}(\omega + t) = \operatorname{sl}[\omega - (-t)] = \operatorname{sl}(-t) = -\operatorname{sl} t.$$

The lemniscate cosine is defined in terms of the sine by

$$\operatorname{cl} t = \operatorname{sl}\left(\frac{\omega}{2} - t\right). \tag{22}$$

From this, it follows in particular that it, too, is a periodic function with period 2ω. However, in contrast with sl t, the function cl t is an even function. To see this, note that, by using successively (22), (21), (19), and again (22), we have

$$\operatorname{cl}(-t) = \operatorname{sl}\left(\frac{\omega}{2} + t\right) = -\operatorname{sl}\left(-\frac{\omega}{2} + t\right) = \operatorname{sl}\left(\frac{\omega}{2} - t\right) = \operatorname{cl} t. \tag{23}$$

The reader can easily verify the following identities:

$$\operatorname{cl}(\omega - t) = -\operatorname{cl} t, \quad \operatorname{cl}(\omega + t) = -\operatorname{cl} t. \tag{24}$$

The definition of the lemniscate functions and equation (16) enable us to answer the question as to the number and nature of solutions of equations of the form sl $t = a$ or cl $t = a$, where a is a real number.

Here, we have a perfect analogy with the case of circular functions (cf. section 1).

For example, let us consider the equation

$$\operatorname{sl} t = a. \tag{25}$$

We may assert that, for $|a| > 1$, it has no solution at all. For $|a| \leqslant 1$, there exists at least one solution in the interval $0 \leqslant t < 2\omega$. Specifically,

if $a = 1$, there is the single solution $t = \frac{\omega}{2}$;

if $0 < a < 1$, there are two solutions, t_1 and t_2;

these are such that $0 < t_1 < \frac{\omega}{2}$ and $\frac{\omega}{2} < t_2 = \omega - t_1 < \omega$;

if $a = 0$, there are two solutions $t_1 = 0$ and $t_2 = \omega$;

if $-1 < a < 0$, there are two solutions t_1 and t_2;

these are such that $\omega < t_1 < \frac{3\omega}{2}$ and $\frac{3\omega}{2} < t_2 = 3\omega - t_1 < 2\omega$;

if $a = -1$, there is the single solution $t = \frac{3\omega}{2}$.

Obviously, in each of the cases $\alpha = 1$ and $\alpha = -1$, we can speak of two solutions that coincide.

We note also that, if $t_1 \neq t_2$, the corresponding values of cl t are negatives of each other:

$$\text{cl } t_1 = -\text{cl } t_2.$$

Geometrically, solution of equation (25) reduces to finding the points of intersection of the lemniscate (16) and the circle $x^2 + y^2 = a^2$, to the choice of those points on the intersection for which $r = OA$ has the same sign as α, and, finally, to the calculation of the corresponding arc lengths.

All that has been said in the present section is illustrated in the graphs of sl t and cl t, which, in appearance, resemble the sine and cosine graphs (see Fig. 10).

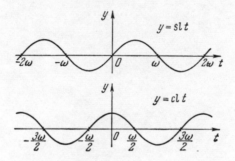

FIG. 10.

Generalized Sines

6. Let us now show that a uniform approach is possible to the study of the sines (and with them the cosines) defined geometrically in Chapter 1. With this end, *we shall consider each type of sine as a function inverse to some integral.*

Let us begin with the circular sine. At the end of section 1, it was noted that the variable t can be interpreted as twice the area of the circular sector OAC (see Fig. 1). If x and $y = \sin t$ are the coordinates of a point A, then $x = \sqrt{1 - y^2}$ and, consequently,

$$\text{area } \triangle OAK = \frac{1}{2} y \sqrt{1 - y^2}.$$

The area of the curvilinear trapezoid $OCAK$ is calculated from the formula

$$\text{area } OCAK = \int_0^y \xi \, d\eta = \int_0^y \sqrt{1 - \eta^2} \, d\eta.$$

Integrating by parts, we obtain

$$\int_0^y \sqrt{1 - \eta^2} \, d\eta = \sqrt{1 - y^2}\, y + \int_0^y \frac{\eta^2 \, d\eta}{\sqrt{1 - \eta^2}} =$$

$$= \sqrt{1 - y^2}\, y - \int_0^y \sqrt{1 - \eta^2} \, d\eta + \int_0^y \frac{d\eta}{\sqrt{1 - \eta^2}},$$

from which we get

$$\int\limits_0^y \sqrt{1-\eta^2}\,d\eta = \frac{1}{2}\sqrt{1-y^2}\,y + \frac{1}{2}\int\limits_0^y \frac{d\eta}{\sqrt{1-\eta^2}}.$$

Consequently,

$$S = \text{area } OCA = \text{area } OCAK - \text{area } \triangle OAK = \frac{1}{2}\int\limits_0^y \frac{d\eta}{\sqrt{1-\eta^2}},$$

or

$$t = 2S = \int\limits_0^y \frac{d\eta}{\sqrt{1-\eta^2}}. \tag{26}$$

As the variable y increases from -1 to 1, the variable t increases from $-\pi/2$ to $\pi/2$. We can calculate $\pi/2$ from the formula

$$\int\limits_0^1 \frac{d\eta}{\sqrt{1-\eta^2}} = \frac{\pi}{2} \approx 1.5708. \tag{27}$$

Conversely, as t increases from $-\pi/2$ to $\pi/2$, the variable $y = \sin t$ increases from -1 to 1. Thus, we can regard the function $y = \sin t$ in the interval $(-\pi/2, \pi/2)$ as the function inverse to the integral (26). As before, the function $\cos t$ is defined by the formula

$$\cos t = \sin\left(\frac{\pi}{2} - t\right).$$

7. Let us now look at the hyperbolic sine sinh t. In defining it geometrically (cf. section 2), we interpreted the variable t as twice the area of the sector OCA (see Fig. 4). We have

$$S = \text{area } OCA = \text{area } OCAK - \text{area } OAK.$$

By using the equation for a hyperbola $x^2 - y^2 = 1$, we find

$$\text{area } OAK = \frac{1}{2}xy = \frac{1}{2}\sqrt{1+y^2}\,y$$

and

$$\text{area } OCAK = \int_0^y \xi \, d\eta = \int_0^y \sqrt{1+\eta^2} \, d\eta.$$

Integration by parts yields

$$\int_0^y \sqrt{1+\eta^2} \, d\eta = \sqrt{1+y^2} \, y - \int_0^y \frac{\eta^2}{\sqrt{1+\eta^2}} \, d\eta =$$

$$= \sqrt{1+y^2} \, y - \int_0^y \sqrt{1+\eta^2} \, d\eta + \int_0^y \frac{d\eta}{\sqrt{1+\eta^2}},$$

so that

$$\text{area } OCAK = \int_0^y \sqrt{1+\eta^2} \, d\eta = \frac{1}{2} \sqrt{1+y^2} \, y + \frac{1}{2} \int_0^y \frac{d\eta}{\sqrt{1+\eta^2}}.$$

Consequently,

$$S = \frac{1}{2} \int_0^y \frac{d\eta}{\sqrt{1+\eta^2}}$$

or

$$t = 2S = \int_0^y \frac{d\eta}{\sqrt{1+\eta^2}}. \tag{28}$$

As the variable y increases from $-\infty$ to $+\infty$, the variable t also increases from $-\infty$ to $+\infty$ since

$$\int_0^\infty \frac{d\eta}{\sqrt{1+\eta^2}} = \infty.$$

Conversely, as t increases from $-\infty$ to $+\infty$, the variable y also increases from $-\infty$ to $+\infty$. Thus, we can regard the function $y = \sinh t$ on the entire real axis $(-\infty, +\infty)$ as the function inverse to the integral (28).

8. In what follows, we shall choose a procedure of exposition in which the integrals (26) and (28) will be the original functions, and the functions $\sin t$ and $\sinh t$ will be secondary, that is, obtained from the preceding. We shall define the latter functions as the inverses of the integrals. Of course, when such definitions are made, the integrals themselves can be regarded as the functions inverse to $\sin t$ and $\sinh t$ and we can introduce the following notations for them:

$$t = \int_0^y \frac{d\eta}{\sqrt{1-\eta^2}} = \arcsin y \text{ and } t = \int_0^y \frac{d\eta}{\sqrt{1+\eta^2}} = \operatorname{arsinh} y.$$

In the first case, the syllable "arc" is appropriate because twice the area of the sector OAC in the unit circle is measured by the same number as is the arc AC. In the second case, the syllable "ar" stands for "area". In the case of the hyperbola, however, there is no such simple relationship between the area of the sector OAC and the arc AC as in the case of a circle.

Finally, formulas (29) do not as yet provide us with new means for calculating the corresponding integrals. For example, the first of them simply asserts that the integral is the function inverse to $\sin t$, but we have decided to define $\sin t$ itself as the function inverse to the integral!

However, for the second of the integrals (2), there is an analytic representation that does not depend on our definitions. Specifically, it is given by the following formula, the validity of which can be shown by differentiating:

$$t = \int_0^y \frac{d\eta}{\sqrt{1+\eta^2}} = \ln\left(y + \sqrt{1+y^2}\right). \tag{30}$$

This enables us to obtain a formula for the inverse function $y = \sinh t$ without needing to resort to the integral (38) every time we need to speak of the hyperbolic sine. Specifically, it follows from (30) that

$$\sqrt{1+y^2} + y = e^t,$$

so that

$$\sqrt{1+y^2} - y = \frac{1}{\sqrt{1+y^2}+y} = e^{-t}.$$

If we subtract the second of these equations from the first, we obtain

$$y = \sinh t = \frac{e^t - e^{-t}}{2}. \tag{31}$$

Thus, it would have been possible at the very beginning to define the hyperbolic sine from formula (31) as half the difference of two exponential functions.

Then, formula (10) for cosh t yields

$$\cosh^2 t = 1 + \left(\frac{e^t - e^{-t}}{2}\right)^2 = \left(\frac{e^t + e^{-t}}{2}\right)^2.$$

Since $(e^t + e^{-t})/2 > 0$ and cosh t is also positive (we recall that $x = \cosh t$ is the abscissa of a point on the right branch of the hyperbola (Fig. 4)), we have

$$\cosh t = \frac{e^t + e^{-t}}{2}. \tag{32}$$

This formula defines the hyperbolic cosine as the average of the exponential functions e^t and e^{-t}. In Chapter 5, we shall see that the circular functions can also be expressed in terms of exponential functions though only with *imaginary* arguments of the exponentials.

9. Let us turn to the lemniscate sine sl t, where the variable t is treated as the arc length of the lemniscate. Let us use polar coordinates for the integral expression for t. In polar coordinates, the differential of the arc length is given (see Fig. 11) by:

$$dt = \sqrt{(r\,d\varphi)^2 + dr^2} = \sqrt{r^2 \left(\frac{d\varphi}{dt}\right)^2 + 1}\; dr.$$

In the present case, equation (17) yields

$$\varphi = \frac{1}{2} \arcsin(r^2).$$

From (29) (with $y = r^2$), we obtain

$$\frac{d\varphi}{dr} = \frac{r}{\sqrt{1 - r^4}}.$$

Consequently,

$$dt = \sqrt{\frac{r^4}{1-r^4} + 1}\, dr = \frac{dr}{\sqrt{1-r^4}},$$

so that

$$t = \int\limits_0^r \frac{dr}{\sqrt{1-r^4}}. \tag{33}$$

As r increases from -1 to $+1$, the integral (33) increases from $-\omega/2$ to $\omega/2$, where $\omega/2$ has the value

$$\frac{\omega}{2} = \int\limits_0^1 \frac{dr}{\sqrt{1-r^4}} \approx 1.3111. \tag{34}$$

Conversely, as t increases from $-\omega/2$ to $\omega/2$, the variable r increases from -1 to 1. Thus, we can define the function $y = \mathrm{sl}\, t$ in the interval $(-\omega/2,\ \omega/2)$ as the function inverse to the integral (33). As before, we shall define the function $\mathrm{cl}\, t$ by the formula

$$\mathrm{cl}\, t = \mathrm{sl}\left(\frac{\omega}{2} - t\right).$$

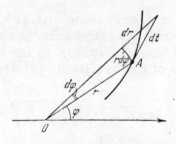

FIG. 11.

10. Let us compare the definitions of the three sines given in this chapter: (1) $y = \sin t$ (the circular sine), the function inverse to the function

$$\int\limits_0^y \frac{d\eta}{\sqrt{1-\eta^2}},$$

and defined in the interval $(-\pi/2, \pi/2)$, where

$$\frac{\pi}{2} = \int_0^1 \frac{d\eta}{\sqrt{1-\eta^2}};$$

(2) $y = \sinh t$ (the hyperbolic sine), the function inverse to

$$\int_0^y \frac{d\eta}{\sqrt{1+\eta^2}},$$

and defined on the entire real axis; (3) $y = \text{sl } t$ (the lemniscate sine) the function inverse to

$$\int_0^y \frac{d\eta}{\sqrt{1-\eta^4}},$$

and defined in the interval $(-\omega/2, \omega/2)$, where

$$\frac{\omega}{2} = \int_0^1 \frac{d\eta}{\sqrt{1-\eta^4}}.$$

Obviously, all these cases will be included if we succeed in studying the function $y = s(t)$ inverse to an integral of the form

$$t = \int_0^y \frac{dy}{\sqrt{1+m\eta^2+n\eta^4}}, \tag{35}$$

where m and n are any real numbers. Let us agree to call such a function a "generalized sine."

For $m = -1$ and $n = 0$, we have the circular sine; for $m = 1$ and $n = 0$, we have the hyperbolic sine; for $m = 0$ and $n = -1$, we have the lemniscate sine.

If $m = -(1+k^2)$ and $n = k^2$, where $0 < k < 1$, the polynomial $1 + m\eta^2 + n\eta^4$ takes the form $(1-\eta^2)(1-k^2\eta^2)$. In this case, the function $s(t)$ is the Jacobian elliptic function with modulus k. It is called the *sine amplitude* and is donated by $\text{sn}(t, k)$ or, more briefly, $\text{sn } t$.

The function $\text{sn } t$ is encountered, for example, in the problem of the pendulum. This problem consists in study of the oscillations, in a vertical plane, of a heavy sphere of mass m at the end of a fine thread of length l (see Fig. 12). Suppose that this thread with the attached sphere is held at an angle θ_0 from its equilibrium position and that the sphere is then released with zero initial velocity.

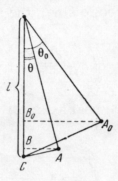

FIG. 12.

When the string is passing through the position that makes an angle θ with the vertical, the velocity of the sphere is $v = l\, d\theta/dt$ and its kinetic energy is

$$\frac{mv^2}{2} = \frac{ml^2}{2}\left(\frac{d\theta}{dt}\right)^2.$$

From the theorem on kinetic energies, this value must be equal in the present case to the work done by gravity (we neglect air resistance):

$$mgB_0B = mgl\,(\cos\theta - \cos\theta_0).$$

Thus,

$$\frac{ml^2}{2}\left(\frac{d\theta}{dt}\right)^2 = mgl\,(\cos\theta - \cos\theta_0),$$

so that

$$dt = -\sqrt{\frac{l}{2g}} \cdot \frac{d\theta}{\sqrt{\cos\theta - \cos\theta_0}}$$

(The minus sign is due to the fact that the angle θ first decreases as t increases). Integrating, we obtain

$$t = -\sqrt{\frac{l}{2g}} \int_{\theta_0}^{\theta} \frac{d\theta}{\sqrt{\cos\theta - \cos\theta_0}} = \sqrt{\frac{l}{2g}} \int_{\theta}^{\theta_0} \frac{d\theta}{\sqrt{\cos\theta - \cos\theta_0}} =$$

$$= \frac{1}{2}\sqrt{\frac{l}{g}} \int_{\theta}^{\theta_0} \frac{d\theta}{\sqrt{\sin^2\frac{\theta_0}{2} - \sin^2\frac{\theta}{2}}}.$$

Let us make the change of variable

$$\sin\frac{\theta}{2} = \sin\frac{\theta_0}{2}\,\eta^2.$$

Obviously, η has a simple geometric interpretation, namely,

$$\eta = \frac{AC}{A_0C}.$$

We obtain

$$t = \sqrt{\frac{l}{g}} \int_{\eta}^{1} \frac{d\eta}{\sqrt{(1-\eta^2)\left(1-\sin^2\frac{\theta_0}{2}\,\eta^2\right)}}.$$

If we denote the constant

$$\sqrt{\frac{l}{g}} \int_{0}^{1} \frac{d\eta}{\sqrt{(1-\eta^2)\left(1-\sin\frac{\theta_0}{2}\,\eta^2\right)}}$$

by t_0 (representing the instant the pendulum passes through its equilibrium position), we can rewrite the last formula in the form

$$t_0 - t = \sqrt{\frac{l}{g}} \int_{0}^{\eta} \frac{d\eta}{\sqrt{(1-\eta^2)\left(1-\sin^2\frac{\theta_0}{2}\,\eta^2\right)}},$$

from which we get

$$\int_{0}^{\eta} \frac{d\eta}{\sqrt{(1-\eta^2)\left(1-\sin^2\frac{\theta_0}{2}\,\eta^2\right)}} = \sqrt{\frac{g}{l}}\,(t_0 - t)$$

and, consequently,

$$\eta = \frac{\sin \frac{\theta}{2}}{\sin \frac{\theta_0}{2}} = \operatorname{sn} \left[\sqrt{\frac{g}{l}} \, (t_0 - t), \ \sin \frac{\theta_0}{2} \right].$$

Thus, we have expressed the quantity η characterizing the displacement of the pendulum at the instant t from its equilibrium position in terms of the Jacobian elliptic function with modulus $k = \sin(\theta_0/2)$.

11. It is natural to require that the polynomial

$$P(\eta) = 1 + m\eta^2 + n\eta^4$$

in formula (35) not be a perfect square. Otherwise, $\sqrt{P(\eta)}$ will be of the form $1 + q\eta^2$, and the integral (35) will be expressed either in terms of the arc tangent (if $q > 0$) or in terms of the logarithm of a linear fractional function (if $q < 0$). In each of these cases, examination of the inverse function would yield nothing new. Therefore, in what follows, we shall assume that

$$m^2 - 4n \neq 0. \tag{36}$$

We also need to distinguish between the following two cases:

I. The polynomial $P(\eta)$ has no real zeros. This means that either the second-degree trinomial $1 + mz + nz^2$ has no real zeros (that is, $m^2 - 4n < 0$) or its zeros are negative real numbers (that is, $m^2 - 4n > 0$, $n > 0$, $m > 0$). In this case, $P(\eta) > 0$ for arbitrary (real) η. Therefore, the integral (35) is defined and represents a strictly increasing function on the entire real axis. We denote the expression

$$\int_0^\infty \frac{d\eta}{\sqrt{1 + m\eta^2 + n\eta^4}}$$

by A. For $n = 0$, this integral diverges and $A = \infty$. For $n \neq 0$, it converges and A is a finite positive number. Since the integral (35) increases continuously from $-A$ to $+A$ as y increases continuously from $-\infty$ to $+\infty$, the inverse function $y = s(t)$ is defined in this case in the interval $(-A, +A)$ and it increases continuously in that interval from $-\infty$ to $+\infty$. The hyperbolic sine (for which $A = \infty$) provides a very simple illustration of this case.

II. The polynomial $P(\eta)$ has real zeros (either two or four such). This means that $m^2 - 4n > 0$ and that either $n < 0$ or $m < 0 < n$. Let α denote the smallest positive zero. Then, $-\alpha$ denotes the negative zero of smallest absolute value. Therefore, the polynomial $P(\eta)$ has no zeros in the interval $(-\alpha, \alpha)$. Hence, $P(\eta)$ does not change sign in that interval; it remains positive since $P(0) = 1 > 0$. [We note that $P(\eta)$ becomes negative when η (increasing) passes through the value α.] The integral (35) is a function that is defined and strictly increasing in the interval $(-\alpha, \alpha)$. We denote the expression

$$\int_0^\alpha \frac{d\eta}{\sqrt{1 + m\eta^2 + n\eta^4}}$$

by a (which is > 0). Since the integral (35) increases continuously from $-a$ to a as y increases continuously from $-\alpha$ to α, the inverse function $y = s(t)$ is defined in this case in the interval $(-a, a)$ and increases continuously in that interval from $-\alpha$ to α. The circular sine (for which $\alpha = 1$ and $a = \pi/2$) are simple illustrations of this case.

In the case of the Jacobian function, in which

$$1 + m\eta^2 + n\eta^4 = (1 - \eta^2)(1 - k^2\eta^2) \qquad (0 < k < 1),$$

we have

$$\alpha = 1. \quad a = \int_0^1 \frac{d\eta}{\sqrt{(1 - \eta^2)(1 - k^2\eta^2)}}.$$

This last quantity is called the complete *elliptic integral of the first kind in Legendre's normal form.* It is denoted by $K(k)$ or, more briefly, by K. Special tables have been compiled for it. We note that there is a simple expression for ω in terms of $K(1/\sqrt{2})$:

$$\frac{\omega}{2} = \int_0^1 \frac{d\eta}{\sqrt{1 - \eta^4}} = \frac{1}{\sqrt{2}} \int_0^1 \frac{d\eta}{\sqrt{(1 - \eta^2)\left(1 - \frac{1 - \eta^2}{2}\right)}}.$$

If we now set $1 - \eta^2 = y^2$, we obtain

$$\frac{\omega}{2} = \frac{1}{\sqrt{2}} \int_0^1 \frac{dy}{\sqrt{(1 - y^2)\left(1 - \frac{1}{2} y^2\right)}} = \frac{1}{\sqrt{2}} K\left(\frac{1}{\sqrt{2}}\right).$$

Thus, if we define the functions sin t, sinh t, sl t, and sn (t, k) as the functions inverse to the integrals referred to above, only the function sinh t is defined on the entire real axis. The functions sin t, sl t, and sn (t, k) are defined only in the finite intervals

$$-\frac{\pi}{2} \leqslant t \leqslant \frac{\pi}{2}; \quad -\frac{\omega}{2} \leqslant t \leqslant \frac{\omega}{2}; \quad -K \leqslant t \leqslant K,$$

respectively.

In the following chapter, we shall show how we can adhere to our basic plan of exposition *in terms of the inverses of integrals* and still extend these definitions not only to arbitrary real intervals but to the field of complex values of t. However, when we do this, the product formulas and the periodicity of the functions sin t and sl t, of which we spoke in Chapter 1, will not be immediately obvious. Nonetheless, an addition theorem, which we shall obtain in Chapter 4, will enable us to establish easily not only these but many other facts that go far beyond what we might discover if we confined ourselves to a geometric definition of these sines.

CHAPTER 3

Integration in the Complex Plane

12. As we have stated, it is possible to study completely the properties of the various sines and their similarities and differences if we treat them as functions of a complex variable $t = \sigma + i\tau$, where σ and τ are real numbers and i is the imaginary unit. Of course, when we do this we cannot then interpret t as area or arc length, nor can we interpret the corresponding value of the sine in question as the ordinate of a point or the length of a chord. At the basis of the definition is the integral

$$t = \int_0^w \frac{dz}{\sqrt{1 + mz^2 + nz^4}}, \tag{37}$$

the upper limit w of which is some complex number $w = u + iv$, where u and v are real numbers.

Let us assume, just as in Chapter 2, that m and n are real numbers such that $m^2 - 4n \neq 0$. The integral (37) is a particular case of an integral of the form

$$\int_0^w R\left(z, \sqrt{a_0 + a_1 z + a_2 z^2 + a_3 z^3 + a_4 z^4}\right) dz, \tag{38}$$

where the integrand is a rational function of z and the square root of a polynomial of no higher than fourth degree. Such an integral is called, in general, an *elliptic integral* (provided the integrand does not reduce to a rational function of z and the

25

square root of a polynomial of second or lower degree). In particular, for the integral (37) to be elliptic, it is necessary that $m^2 - 4n \neq 0$ and that $n \neq 0$. The name "elliptic" is due to the fact that the length of an arc of an ellipse is expressed in terms of an integral of the form (38). In particular, if $x^2/a^2 + y^2/b^2 = 1$ (where $(b \neq a)$ is the equation of a particular ellipse, the length of the arc CA (see Fig. 13) is represented by the integral

$$\widehat{CA} = \int_x^a \sqrt{1 + \left(\frac{dy}{dx}\right)^2} \, dx = \int_x^a \sqrt{1 + \frac{b^2 x^2}{a^2 (a^2 - x^2)}} \, dx =$$

$$= \frac{1}{a} \int_x^a \frac{a^4 - (a^2 - b^2) x^2}{\sqrt{(a^2 - x^2) [a^4 - (a^2 - b^2) x^2]}} \, dx.$$

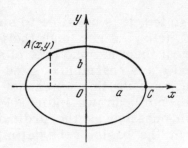

FIG. 13.

13. Let us pause to see how we should interpret the integral (37) in the case in which w is a complex number and what properties this integral possesses. Here, we shall make certain assertions without proof. Proofs can be found in most textbooks on the theory of functions of a complex variable.

Let us set up a Cartesian coordinate system in the plane. We shall regard (x, y) as the image of the complex number $z = x + iy$. In what follows, we shall apply the term "point" both to a point in the complex plane and to the complex number corresponding to it.

Let us connect the coordinate origin $z = 0$ with any point $w = u + iv$ by drawing a continuous curve L of finite length from the origin to the point w (see Fig. 14). (The fact that the curve starts at the coordinate origin is of no significance for the derivations that we are going to make.) Let us partition L into arcs by choosing points $z_0 = 0$, z_1, z_2, ..., z_{n-1}, $z_n = w$ numbered in the direction of motion along L from 0 to w, and let us form the corresponding approximating sum for the function $1/\sqrt{1+mz^2+nz^4}$:

$$\sum_{k=1}^{n} \frac{1}{\sqrt{1+mz_k^2+nz_k^4}}(z_k - z_{k-1}). \tag{39}$$

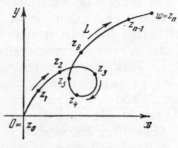

FIG. 14.

Since $\sqrt{1+mz^2+nz^4}$ is a double-valued function, let us agree that, for $z = z_0 = 0$, we take the positive square root of 1. Suppose also that, if the value of the square root has been chosen at any point z_{k-1}, that value at the point z_k is chosen that will be the closer to the value at z_{k-1}. Then, for an arbitrary partition of the curve L, the sum (39) will have a definite value. Let us now take over finer partitions of L so that the length of the longest arc approaches zero. It can be shown that the sum (39) will approach a definite limit. It is called the integral of $1/\sqrt{1+mz^2+nz^4}$ along L and is denoted by

$$\int_{L} \frac{dz}{\sqrt{1+mz^2+mz^4}}. \tag{40}$$

If the point w lies on the real x-axis (that is, if $w = u$ and $v = 0$), if the polynomial $1+mz^2+nz^1$ does not vanish anywhere on the interval $[0, u]$, and if L coincides with this interval, then all the values of z, that is, $z_0 = 0$, $z_1, \ldots, z_n$, are real numbers, the values of $\sqrt{1+mz_j^2+nz_j^4}$ are real and positive, and we have simply the usual definite integral

$$\int_{0}^{u} \frac{dx}{\sqrt{1+mx^2+nx^4}}.$$

In analogy with the general case, it is customary to write the integral (40) in the form

$$\int_0^w \frac{dz}{\sqrt{1 + mz^2 + nz^4}},\tag{41}$$

without indicating the curve L over which the integration is taken (that is, for the points of which the approximating sums (39) are formed). However, such notation causes some indefiniteness. Specifically, for two distinct curves L_1 and L_2 that unite the points 0 and w, the corresponding integrals (40) may have distinct values. However, in the study of the theory of functions of a complex variable, it is shown that this can happen only when the curves L_1 and L_2 encircle one or more zeros of the polynomial $1 + mz^2 + nz^4$ (at which the integrand becomes infinite) one or more times. [See Fig. 15, where β_1 and β_2 represent two of the four zones of that polynomial and the curves L_1 and L_2 together encircle both these zeros twice.] Here, the difference between the two values of the integral depends on just how many zeros are encircled and how many times they are encircled. Therefore, the integral (41) has infinitely many distinct values for every value of w; that is, it represents a multiple-valued function $F(w)$, any one of the values of which we shall denote by the letter t (where t is a complex number):

$$t = \int_0^w \frac{dz}{\sqrt{1 + mz^2 + nz^4}} = F(w).\tag{42}$$

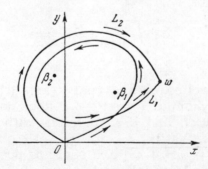

FIG. 15.

Let us suppose that w_0 does not coincide with any zero of the polynomial $1 + mw^2 + nw^4$, that is,

$$1 + mw_0^2 + nw_0^4 \neq 0.$$

Then, we can draw a circle K around w_0 that will also encircle no zero of that polynomial (see Fig. 16). Let us choose any curve L_0 connecting $z = 0$ with w_0. For points w inside the circle K, let us take curves formed by the union of L_0 and the line segment drawn from w_0 to w. Under these supplementary conditions, the integral (42) defines a single-valued function of w inside the circle, which coincides with some single-valued branch of the function $F(w)$ inside the circle K. Its value at the point w is equal to the integral along L_0 plus the integral along the segment $w_0 w$. To switch to any other branch, we need only replace the curve L_0 with another curve L_0' to which another value of the integral at the point w_0 corresponds. It is easy to see that the corresponding branches differ by a constant term inside K. One can show that each of these branches possesses a derivative at an arbitrary point w inside the circle K; specifically,

$$\frac{dt}{dw} = \lim_{w_1 \in w} \frac{t_1 - t}{w_1 - w} = \frac{1}{\sqrt{1 + mw^2 + nw^4}}. \tag{43}$$

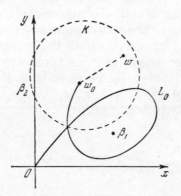

FIG. 16.

In other words, the theorem that the derivative with respect to the upper limit of integration of an integral is equal to the value of the integrand at the corresponding point remains valid for the complex integral (42).

Furthermore, one can show that none of the values of our integral that are assumed at any point w_1 in the plane can coincide with any of the values of the integral assumed at another point w_2 (where $w_2 \neq w_1$). In other words, to a given value t of the integral there corresponds only one point w as the upper limit of integration.*

All this justifies our regarding w in formula (42) as a single-valued function of the complex variable t. That is, *we may regard the upper limit of integration as a function of the value of the integral.* Let us denote this function by

$$w = s(t). \tag{44}$$

As before, we shall call it a generalized sine.

It follows from (43) that

$$dw = \sqrt{1 + mw^2 + nw^4}\, dt. \tag{45}$$

With regard to the multiple-valuedness of the integral (42), which results from the fact that to a single value of w there corresponds infinitely many distinct values of t, this property leads to the following assertion for the inverse function (44). A single value of w is obtained for infinitely many distinct values of t. In connection with this, we shall see in Chapter 6 that the function $s(t)$ is a periodic function of t.

14. Let us compare the values of the integral (42) corresponding to two points w and $-w$ symmetric about the coordinate origin. Let us connect these two points with the origin by curves L and L' that are symmetric about the origin (see Fig. 17), and let us integrate over these curves from the origin to the points w and $-w$, respectively. If we partition the curve L into arcs by means of the points $z_0 = 0$, z_1, z_2, ..., $z_n = w$ and evaluate the corresponding approximating sum

$$\sum_{k=1}^{n} \frac{1}{\sqrt{1 + mz_k^2 + nz_k^4}} (z_k - z_{k-1}), \tag{46}$$

and if we partition the curve L' into symmetric arcs with the aid of the symmetric points $-z_0 = 0$, $-z_1$, $-z_2$, ..., $-z_n = -w$ and again evaluate the approximating sum,

$$\sum_{k=1}^{n} \frac{1}{\sqrt{1 + mz_k^2 + nz_k^4}} (-z_k + z_{k-1}) \tag{46'}$$

*A detailed proof of this fact can be found in E. Goursat, *A Course in Mathematical Analysis*, vol. II, New York, Dover, 1959. However, this proof assumes familiarity with the general theory of analytic functions and the fundamentals of the theory of elliptic functions.

the values of the second sum will differ in sign from the preceding one. But the first of these has the limit

$$\int_{L}^{\cdot} \frac{dz}{\sqrt{1 + mz^2 + nz^4}}$$

which is one of the values of

$$\int_{0}^{w} \frac{dz}{\sqrt{1 + mz^2 + nz^4}},$$

and the second has the limit

$$\int_{L'}^{\cdot} \frac{dz}{\sqrt{1 + nz^2 + nz^4}}$$

which is one of the values of

$$\int_{0}^{-w} \frac{dz}{\sqrt{1 + mz^2 + nz^4}}.$$

It is clear from what has been said that these values differ from
each other only in sign. In other words, if

$$\int_{0}^{w} \frac{dz}{\sqrt{1 + mz^2 + nz^i}} = t,$$

then

$$\int_{0}^{-w} \frac{dz}{\sqrt{1 + mz^2 + nz^4}} = -t.$$

(We are still assuming that the integration is over two curves
symmetric with respect to each other about the point $z = 0$.)
From this it follows that, if the value of the upper limit w
corresponds to the value of the integral t, then the upper limit
$-w$ corresponds to the value $-t$. In other words, if

$$s(t) = w$$

then

$$s(-t) = -w,$$

that is,

$$s(-t) = -s(t). \tag{47}$$

This means that the function $s(t)$, representing the inverse of the integral (42), is an odd function.

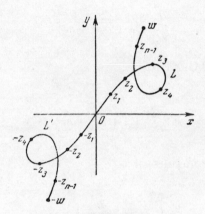

FIG. 17.

15. In the preceding section, we compared the values of the integral along the curves L and L', where L' was obtained from L by a rotation through the angle π about the coordinate origin. Now, let us compare the values of the integrals along the curves L and L'', where L'' is obtained from L by rotating it through an angle $\pi/2$ about the coordinate origin (see Fig. 18). We note that this rotation corresponds to multiplication of each point of the curve L (that is, the complex number represented by each point) by the number i.

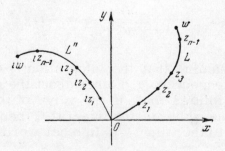

FIG. 18.

Obviously, if the curve L connects the origin with the point w, then L'' connects the origin with the point iw.

Let us partition the curve L into arcs separated at the points $z_0 = 0$, z_1, z_2, ..., z_{n-1}, $z_n = w$. For the function $1/\sqrt{1 + mz^2 + nz^4}$, the corresponding approximating sum is

$$\sum_{k=1}^{n} \frac{1}{\sqrt{1 + mz_k^2 + nz_k^4}} (z_k - z_{k-1}). \qquad (48)$$

The points obtained from the above-listed points by means of a rotation through $\pi/2$ about the coordinate origin lie on the curve L''. These are the points $iz_0 = 0$, iz_1, iz_2, ..., iz_{n-1}, $iz_n = iw$. The corresponding approximating sum for the same function $1/\sqrt{1 + mz^2 + mz^4}$ is of the form

$$\sum_{k=1}^{n} \frac{1}{\sqrt{1 - mz_k^2 + nz_k^4}} \cdot (iz_k - iz_{k-1}). \qquad (49)$$

If the partition of the curve L is varied in such a way that the length of the longest arc $z_{k-1}z_k$ approaches 0, the first approximating sum will approach the limit

$$\int_L \frac{dz}{\sqrt{1 + mz^2 + nz^4}},$$

which represents one of the values of the multiple-valued function

$$\int_0^w \frac{dz}{\sqrt{1 + mz^2 + nz^4}}.$$

Comparison of (49) and (48) shows that (49) can be regarded as the approximating sum constructed for the same curve but for a different function, namely, the function

$$\frac{i}{\sqrt{1 - mz_k^2 + nz_k^4}}.$$

Therefore, the limit (49) is equal to the integral

$$i \int_L \frac{dz}{\sqrt{1 - mz^2 + nz^4}},$$

which represents one of the values of the multiple-valued function

$$i \int_0^w \frac{dz}{\sqrt{1 - mz^2 + mz^4}}.$$

On the other hand, this same limit must be equal to the integral

$$\int_{L''} \frac{dz}{\sqrt{1 + mz^2 + nz^4}}$$

which is one of the values of

$$\int_0^{iw} \frac{dz}{\sqrt{1 + mz^2 + mz^4}}$$

since the approximating sum (49) was constructed for the curve L'' and the function

$$\frac{1}{\sqrt{1 + mz^2 + nz^4}}.$$

From what has been said, it follows that for every value of the integral

$$\int_0^{iw} \frac{dz}{\sqrt{1 + mz^2 + nz^4}}$$

there corresponds the equal value of the integral

$$i \int_0^w \frac{dz}{\sqrt{1 - mz^2 + nz^4}}.$$

In other words, if

$$\int_0^{iw} \frac{dz}{\sqrt{1 + mz^2 + mz^4}} = t \text{ and } \int_0^w \frac{dz}{\sqrt{1 - mz^2 + nz^4}} = t^*,$$

then $t = it^*$ under the hypothesis that the integration in the first integral is over the curve L'' obtained from the curve L, over which the second integral is taken, by rotating L through an angle $\pi/2$ about the coordinate origin.

Let us denote $s^*(t)$ the function inverse to the integral

$$\int_0^w \frac{dz}{\sqrt{1 - mz^2 + nz^4}}.$$

Obviously, $s^*(t)$ is also a generalized sine. It follows from the equation

$$\int_0^w \frac{dz}{\sqrt{1 - mz^2 + nz^4}} = t^*$$

that $w^* = s^*(t^*)$. Also, $lw = s(t)$ and $t = lt^*$. Therefore,

$$s(t) = s(lt^*) = lw = ls^*(t^*).$$

Finally, if we drop the asterisk in the notation t^*, we have

$$s(lt) = ls^*(t). \tag{50}$$

This relationship connects the values of two generalized sines, the first representing the inverse of the integral

$$\int_0^w \frac{dz}{\sqrt{1 + mz^2 + nz^4}},$$

and the second representing the integral

$$\int_0^w \frac{dz}{\sqrt{1 - mz^2 + nz^4}}.$$

16. Using these facts, in what follows we shall consider each of the special cases of the generalized sine as a function of a complex variable. Specifically, the circular sine $w = \sin t$ is the function inverse to the integral

$$t = \int_0^w \frac{dz}{\sqrt{1 - z^2}};$$

the hyperbolic sine $w = \sinh t$ is the function inverse to the integral

$$t = \int_0^w \frac{dz}{\sqrt{1+z^2}};$$

the lemniscate sine $w = \mathrm{sl}\, t$ is the function inverse to the integral

$$t = \int_0^w \frac{dz}{\sqrt{1-z^4}};$$

the Jacobian elliptic function (the sine amplitude) $w = \mathrm{sn}(t, k)$ is the function inverse to the integral

$$t = \int_0^w \frac{dz}{\sqrt{(1-z^2)(1-k^2z^2)}} \qquad (0 < k < 1).$$

If t assumes real values, we can assert that the functions $\sin t$, $\sinh t$, and $\mathrm{sl}\, t$ defined here coincide with the functions of Chapter 1 only in those intervals in which these last functions are inverses of the corresponding integrals. For $\sin t$, this means that $-\pi/2 \leqslant t \leqslant \pi/2$ and, for $\mathrm{sl}\, t$, that $-\omega/2 \leqslant t \leqslant \omega/2$. Only for $\sinh t$ are we without any such restriction; in this case, the integral has an inverse for the entire real axis (cf. Chapter 2).

From section 14, it follows that each of these functions is odd:

$$\begin{aligned} \sin(-t) &= -\sin t, & \sinh(-t) &= -\sinh t, \\ \mathrm{sl}(-t) &= -\mathrm{sl}\, t, & \mathrm{sn}(-t) &= -\mathrm{sn}\, t. \end{aligned} \tag{51}$$

To use the derivations of section 15, we need to consider the function $s(t)$ together with the function $s^*(t)$. The change from $s(t)$ to $s^*(t)$ corresponds to change of sign of the coefficient of z^2 in the polynomial $1 + mz^2 + nz^4$ in the integrand. To see this clearly, we present the following table of type $s(t)$ and $s^*(t)$ functions corresponding to the four particular cases that we are considering.

Integral	Inverse	Integral	Inverse
$\displaystyle\int_0^w \frac{dz}{\sqrt{1-mz^2+nz^4}}$	$s\,(t)$	$\displaystyle\int_0^w \frac{dz}{\sqrt{1-mz^2+nz^4}}$	$s^*\,(t)$
$\displaystyle\int_0^w \frac{dz}{\sqrt{1-z^2}}$	$\sin t$	$\displaystyle\int_0^w \frac{dz}{\sqrt{1+z^2}}$	$\sinh t$
$\displaystyle\int_0^w \frac{dz}{\sqrt{1+z^2}}$	$\mathrm{sh}\,t$	$\displaystyle\int_0^w \frac{dz}{\sqrt{1-z^2}}$	$\sin t$
$\displaystyle\int_0^w \frac{dz}{\sqrt{1-z^4}}$	$\mathrm{sl}\,t$	$\displaystyle\int_0^w \frac{dz}{\sqrt{1-z^4}}$	$\mathrm{sl}\,t$
$\displaystyle\int_0^w \frac{dz}{\sqrt{(1-z^2)(1-k^2z^2)}}$	$\mathrm{sn}\,(t,\,k)$	$\displaystyle\int_0^w \frac{dz}{\sqrt{(1+z^2)(1+k^2z^2)}}$	$\mathrm{sn}^*\,(t,\,k)$

If we apply to each of these particular cases the general formula (50), we find

$$\sin\,(it) = i \sinh t, \tag{52}$$

$$\sinh\,(it) = i \sin t, \tag{53}$$

$$\mathrm{sl}\,(it) = i\,\mathrm{sl}\,t, \tag{54}$$

$$\mathrm{sn}\,(it,\,k) = i\,\mathrm{sn}^*\,(t,\,k). \tag{55}$$

It is easy to see that formulas (51) follow from these last formulas. For example, from formulas (52) and (53) applied successively, we obtain

$$\sin\,(-t) = \sin\,[i\,(it)] = i \sinh\,(it) = i \cdot i \sin t = -\sin t.$$

17. The results of sections 14 and 15 can be obtained in a very simple manner if we assume that the familiar rule of change of variable under the integral sign is also applicable to integrals of functions of a complex variable. In courses on the theory of functions of a complex variable, it is shown that this rule is indeed applicable under quite broad conditions—conditions that are satisfied by the examples we have been considering.

In the integral

$$\int_0^w \frac{dz}{\sqrt{1 + mz^2 + nz^4}}$$

let us make the change $z = -\zeta$. We obtain

$$t = \int_0^w \frac{dz}{\sqrt{1 + mz^2 + nz^4}} = -\int_0^{-w} \frac{d\zeta}{\sqrt{1 + m\zeta^2 + n\zeta^4}}.$$

Turning to the inverse functions, we conclude that

$$w = s(t), \quad -w = s(-t), \quad \text{i.e.,} \quad s(-t) = -s(t).$$

If we make a different substitution, namely, $z = -i\zeta$, that is, $\zeta = iz$, we obtain

$$t = \int_0^w \frac{dz}{\sqrt{1 + mz^2 + nz^4}} = -\int_0^{iw} \frac{i\,d\zeta}{\sqrt{1 - m\zeta^2 + n\zeta^4}}.$$

When we turn to the inverse functions, we conclude that

$$w = s(t), \quad iw = s(it), \quad \text{i.e.,} \quad s(it) = is(t).$$

Let us use once more the rule for change of variable, this time to express the function $\operatorname{sn}^*(t, k)$ representing the inverse of the integral

$$\int_0^w \frac{dz}{\sqrt{(1 + z^2)(1 + k^2 z^2)}} \qquad (0 < k < 1),$$

in terms of the Jacobian function $\operatorname{sn} t$ with appropriate modulus. To do this, we make the following change of variable $z = \zeta/\sqrt{1 - \zeta^2}$. After some simplifications, we obtain

$$\int_0^w \frac{dz}{\sqrt{(1 + z^2)(1 + k^2 z^2)}} = \int_0^{\frac{w}{\sqrt{1 + w^2}}} \frac{d\zeta}{\sqrt{(1 - \zeta^2)[1 - (1 - k^2)\zeta^2]}}.$$

Let us set $k' = \sqrt{1 - k^2} > 0$ (where k' is called the modulus complementary to k). Then, the equation

$$t = \int_0^w \frac{dz}{\sqrt{(1 + z^2)(1 + k^2 z^2)}} \, ,$$

which indicates that $w = \operatorname{sn}^*(t, k)$, can be rewritten

$$t = \int_0^{\frac{w}{\sqrt{1 + w^2}}} \frac{d\zeta}{\sqrt{(1 - \zeta^2)(1 - k'^2 \zeta^2)}} \, ,$$

from which we get

$$\frac{w}{\sqrt{1 + w^2}} = \operatorname{sn}(t, k')$$

or

$$w = \operatorname{sn}^*(t, k) = \frac{\operatorname{sn}^2(t, k')}{\sqrt{1 - \operatorname{sn}^2(t, k')}} \, .$$

Therefore, equation (55) can be replaced with the equation

$$\operatorname{sn}(it, k) = i \frac{\operatorname{sn}(t, k')}{\sqrt{1 - \operatorname{sn}^2(t, k')}} \, , \qquad (55')$$

where $k' = \sqrt{1 - k^2}$.

CHAPTER 4

Euler's Method of Deriving the
Addition Theorems

18. At the basis of all trigonometry lie the two addition theorems

$$\left.\begin{array}{l} \sin(\alpha+\beta) = \sin\alpha\cos\beta + \cos\alpha\sin\beta, \\ \cos(\alpha+\beta) = \cos\alpha\cos\beta - \sin\alpha\sin\beta. \end{array}\right\} \qquad (56)$$

With the aid of the relationship between the sine and cosine, we can rewrite these addition theorems in such a way that the value of $\sin(\alpha+\beta)$ is expressed only in terms of $\sin\alpha$ and $\sin\beta$ and the value of $\cos(\alpha+\beta)$ is expressed only in terms of $\cos\alpha$ and $\cos\beta$:

$$\begin{array}{l} \sin(\alpha+\beta) = \sin\alpha\sqrt{1-\sin^2\beta} + \sqrt{1-\sin^2\alpha}\,\sin\beta, \\ \cos(\alpha+\beta) = \cos\alpha\cos\beta - \sqrt{1-\cos^2\alpha}\,\sqrt{1-\cos^2\beta}. \end{array} \qquad (56')$$

We do not write the $\pm$ sign in front of the radical, but it should be understood that the sign is taken according to the value of the circular function expressed by that root. For example,

$$\sqrt{1-\sin^2\frac{\pi}{6}} = \cos\frac{\pi}{6} = \frac{\sqrt{3}}{2},$$

$$\sqrt{1-\sin^2\frac{3\pi}{4}} = \cos\frac{3\pi}{4} = -\frac{\sqrt{2}}{2} \quad \text{etc.}$$

Each of formulas (56') expresses algebraically the value of the function of the sum of two numbers in terms in the values of

41

that same function of the two individual numbers. Formulas of this type are called *algebraic addition theorems* and we say that a function for which such a theorem is applicable possesses or obeys an algebraic addition theorem. Thus, the sine and cosine obey algebraic addition theorems. Other examples are the linear function $y = at$ and the exponential function $y = e^t$. These are examples since

$$a(\alpha + \beta) = a\alpha + a\beta, \quad e^{\alpha+\beta} = e^\alpha \cdot c^\beta.$$

19. Our next problem will be to derive an addition theorem for the function $w = s(t)$ inverse to the integral

$$t = \int_0^w \frac{dz}{\sqrt{1 + mz^2 + nz^4}}.$$

In particular, we shall obtain addition theorems for sin t, sinh t, sl t, and sn (t, k). In this section, we shall observe the general behavior of the solution of this problem.

Suppose that α and β are arbitrary complex numbers and let us define $\gamma = \alpha + \beta$. We set

$$u = s(\alpha), \quad v = s(\beta), \quad w = s(\alpha + \beta).$$

This means that

$$\alpha = \int_0^u \frac{dy}{\sqrt{1 + my^2 + ny^4}}, \quad \beta = \int_0^v \frac{dy}{\sqrt{1 + my^2 + ny^4}}, \\ \gamma = \int_0^w \frac{dy}{\sqrt{1 + my^2 + ny^4}}. \tag{57}$$

If α and β vary in such a way that their sum γ remains constant:

$$\alpha + \beta = \gamma = \text{const}, \tag{58}$$

then

$$d(\alpha + \beta) = 0,$$

that is,

$$d\left(\int_0^u \frac{dy}{\sqrt{1 + my^2 + ny^4}} + \int_0^v \frac{dy}{\sqrt{1 + my^2 + ny^4}} \right) = 0,$$

or

$$\frac{du}{\sqrt{1 + mu^2 + nu^4}} + \frac{dv}{\sqrt{1 + mv^2 + nv^4}} = 0. \tag{59}$$

This is a differential equation connecting the values $u = s(\alpha)$ and $v = s(\beta)$ subject to the condition (58). We shall show below that equation (59) has an algebraic solution and we shall find it. More precisely, we shall find an algebraic function $F(u, v)$ that is equal to u at $v = 0$ (and equal to v at $u = 0$), the differential of which vanishes by virtue of condition (59) (or (58)). In other words, we shall show that (58) implies that

$$dF(u, v) = 0 \quad \text{and} \quad F(u, v) = C = \text{const.} \tag{60}$$

To find the constant C, we set $\beta = 0$. Then $v = s(\beta)$ vanishes and $F(u, v)$ coincides with $u = s(\alpha)$. But, if $\beta = 0$, it follows on the basis of (58) that $\alpha = \gamma$ and hence $u = s(\alpha) = s(\gamma)$, so that

$$C = F(u, v)\big|_{\beta=0} = u\big|_{\alpha=\gamma} = s(\gamma).$$

Thus,

$$F(u, v) = F[s(\alpha), s(\beta)] = s(\gamma) = s(\alpha + \beta).$$

This relation is independent of the value of the sum $\alpha + \beta = \gamma$. Consequently, we shall obtain an algebraic addition theorem for the function $s(t)$:

$$s(\alpha + \beta) = F[s(\alpha), s(\beta)].$$

Thus, the problem of deriving an algebraic addition theorem for the function $s(t)$ reduces to finding an integral of equation (59) possessing the properties listed.

20. To find an algebraic solution of equation (59), we shall use a method proposed by Euler in his Institutiones Calculi Integralis, Vol. I (1768).* We shall begin with the following fourth-degree algebraic equation relating the variables u and v and containing three arbitrary parameters A, B, and C:

$$u^2 + v^2 + Au^2v^2 + 2Buv - C^2 = 0. \tag{61}$$

---

*Here, we shall use a simplified form of Euler's method that will be sufficient for our purposes.

If we differentiate this equation, we obtain

$$(u + Bv + Auv^2)\, du + (v + Bu + Au^2v)\, dv = 0. \tag{62}$$

But, if we rewrite (61) in the form

$$(Av^2 + 1)\, u^2 + 2Bvu + (v^2 - C^2) = 0,$$

multiply both sides by $Av^2 + 1$, and complete the square, we obtain

$$[(Av^2 + 1)\, u + Bv]^2 - [(C^2 - v^2)(Av^2 + 1) + B^2v^2] = 0,$$

from which we get

$$u + Bv + Auv^2 = \sqrt{C^2 + (B^2 + AC^2 - 1)\, v^2 - Av^4}. \tag{61'}$$

Again, we do not write the $\pm$ sign but we understand whichever of the two values of the square root coincides with the expression on the left. (An analogous remark will apply also to the functions that we shall consider below when we encounter square roots.)

Equation (61) is symmetric in u and v. Therefore, if we reverse the roles of u and v, we obtain from (61')

$$v + Bu + Au^2v = \sqrt{C^2 + (B^2 + AC^2 - 1)\, u^2 - Au^4}. \tag{61''}$$

If we substitute (61') and (61″) into (62), we obtain

$$\sqrt{C^2 + (B^2 + AC^2 - 1)\, v^2 - Av^4}\, du +$$
$$+ \sqrt{C^2 + (B^2 + AC^2 - 1)\, u^2 - Au^4}\, dv = 0$$

or

$$\frac{du}{\sqrt{C^2 + (B^2 + AC^2 - 1)\, u^2 - Au^4}} +$$
$$+ \frac{dv}{\sqrt{C^2 + (B^2 + AC^2 - 1)\, v^4 - Av^4}} = 0. \tag{59'}$$

Since the differential equation (59') is satisfied for all values of u and v that are related by the algebraic relation (61), it follows that (61) is an algebraic solution of (59').

Let us now choose A, B, and C so that equation (59′) will coincide with equation (59) of the preceding section. To do this, we only need to set

$$B^2 + AC^2 - 1 = mC^2, \quad A = -nC^2.$$

Let us express A and B in terms of m, n, and C. Then, equation (59′) (after we multiply all terms by C) takes the form

$$\frac{du}{\sqrt{1 + mu^2 + nu^4}} + \frac{dv}{\sqrt{1 + mv^2 + nv^4}} = 0, \tag{59}$$

and its solution (61) is

$$u^2 + v^2 - nC^2 u^2 v^2 + 2\sqrt{1 + mC^2 + nC^4}\, uv - C^2 = 0, \tag{63}$$

where C is an arbitrary constant.

Since we wish to represent (63) in the form (60) (that is, in the form $F(u, v) = C$), let us solve equation (63) for C. We obtain successively

$$[u^2 + v^2 - (nu^2 v^2 + 1) C^2]^2 = 4(1 + mC^2 + nC^4)\, u^2 v^2,$$

$$(1 - nu^2 v^2)^2 C^4 - 2[(1 + nu^2 v^2)(u^2 + v^2) + \\ + 2mu^2 v^2] C^2 + (u^2 - v^2)^2 = 0,$$

$$C^2 = \frac{(1 + nu^2 v^2)(u^2 + v^2) + 2mu^2 v^2}{(1 - nu^2 v^2)^2} + \\ + \frac{\sqrt{[(1 + nu^2 v^2)(u^2 + v^2) + 2mu^2 v^2]^2 - (u^2 - v^2)^2 (1 - nu^2 v^2)^2}}{(1 - nu^2 v^2)^2} = \\ = \frac{u^2(1 + mv^2 + nv^4) + v^2(1 + mu^2 + nu^4)}{(1 - nu^2 v^2)^2} + \\ + \frac{2uv\sqrt{(1 + mu^2 + nu^4)(1 + mv^2 + nv^4)}}{(1 - nu^2 v^2)^2},$$

so that, finally,

$$\frac{u\sqrt{1 + mv^2 + nv^4} + v\sqrt{1 + mu^2 + nu^4}}{1 - nu^2 v^2} = C. \tag{64}$$

The function

$$F(u, v) = \frac{u\sqrt{1 + mv^2 + nv^4} + v\sqrt{1 + mu^2 + nu^4}}{1 - nu^2 v^2}$$

is algebraic. At $v = 0$, it becomes u and, at $u = 0$, it becomes v. We leave the reader to verify that its differential is of the form

$$dF(u, v) = \Phi(u, v)\left(\frac{du}{\sqrt{1 + mu^2 + nu^4}} + \frac{dv}{\sqrt{1 + mv^2 + nv^4}}\right),$$

where $\Phi(u, v)$ is some nonzero algebraic function. Therefore, the differential equation (59) implies

$$dF(u, v) = 0, \quad \text{or} \quad F(u, v) \equiv \text{const.}$$

Thus, the existence of an algebraic solution of equation (59) possessing the properties indicated in section 19 is established. From this, as was shown in section 19, we get an algebraic addition theorem for $s(t)$ in the form

$$s(\alpha + \beta) = F[s(\alpha), s(\beta)],$$

that is,

$$s(\alpha + \beta) = \frac{s(\alpha)\sqrt{1 + ms^2(\beta) + ns^4(\beta)} + s(\beta)\sqrt{1 + ms^2(\alpha) + ns^4(\alpha)}}{1 - ns^2(\alpha)s^2(\beta)} =$$

$$= \frac{s^2(\alpha) - s^2(\beta)}{s(\alpha)\sqrt{1 + ms^2(\beta) + ns^4(\beta)} - s(\beta)\sqrt{1 + ms^2(\alpha) + ns^4(\alpha)}} . \tag{65}$$

21. From the general addition theorem (65), which is valid for the function $s(t)$, we obtain as special cases the addition theorems for $\sin t$, $\sinh t$, $\operatorname{sl} t$, and $\operatorname{sn}(t, k)$. Corresponding to the circular sine are the values $m = -1$ and $n = 0$; corresponding to the hyperbolic sinc are the values $m = 1$ and $n = 0$; corresponding to the lemniscate sine are the values $m = 0$ and $n = -1$; corresponding to the Jacobian function are the values $m = -(1 + k^2)$ and $n = k^2$ (for $0 < k < 1$).

Accordingly, from formulas (65), we obtain the following addition theorems:

For the circular sine,

$$\sin(\alpha + \beta) = \sin \alpha \sqrt{1 - \sin^2 \beta} + \sin \beta \sqrt{1 - \sin^2 \alpha}; \tag{65'}$$

for the hyperbolic sine,

$$\sinh(\alpha + \beta) = \sinh \alpha \sqrt{1 + \sinh^2 \beta} + \sinh \beta \sqrt{1 + \sinh^2 \alpha}; \tag{65''}$$

for the lemniscate sine,

$$\operatorname{sl}(\alpha + \beta) = \frac{\operatorname{sl} \alpha \sqrt{1 - \operatorname{sl}^4 \beta} + \operatorname{sl} \beta \sqrt{1 - \operatorname{sl}^4 \alpha}}{1 + \operatorname{sl}^2 \alpha \operatorname{sl}^2 \beta} =$$

$$= \frac{\operatorname{sl}^2 \alpha - \operatorname{sl}^2 \beta}{\operatorname{sl} \alpha \sqrt{1 - \operatorname{sl}^4 \beta} - \operatorname{sl} \beta \sqrt{1 - \operatorname{sl}^4 \alpha}}; \tag{65'''}$$

for the function $\mathrm{sn}\,(t,\,k)$,

$$\mathrm{sn}\,(\alpha+\beta)=$$
$$=\frac{\mathrm{sn}\,\alpha\,\sqrt{1+m\,\mathrm{sn}^2\,\beta+n\,\mathrm{sn}^4\,\beta}+\mathrm{sn}\,\beta\,\sqrt{1+m\,\mathrm{sn}^2\,\alpha+n\,\mathrm{sn}^4\,\alpha}}{1-n\,\mathrm{sn}^2\,\alpha\,\mathrm{sn}^2\,\beta}=$$
$$=\frac{\mathrm{sn}^2\,\alpha-\mathrm{sn}^2\,\beta}{\mathrm{sn}\,\alpha\,\sqrt{1+m\,\mathrm{sn}^2\,\beta+n\,\mathrm{sn}^4\,\beta}-\mathrm{sn}\,\beta\,\sqrt{1+m\,\mathrm{sn}^2\,\alpha+n\,\mathrm{sn}^4\,\alpha}}. \qquad (65^{\mathrm{IV}})$$

For brevity, we write $\mathrm{sn}\,(\alpha+\beta)$ instead of $\mathrm{sn}\,(\alpha+\beta,\,k)$ and $\mathrm{sn}\,\alpha$ instead of $\mathrm{sn}\,(\alpha,\,k)$, etc.

It is important to note that α and β in these formulas are *arbitrary complex numbers* except that the α and β in formulas $(65''')$ and (65^{IV}) are such that the denominators of the fractions are nonzero.

Further Study of Complex Values
of the Argument

22. For real values of t, we have the formulas

$$\cos t = \sqrt{1 - \sin^2 t}, \quad \cosh t = \sqrt{1 + \sinh^2 t}, \tag{66}$$

where corresponding to the value $t = 0$ is the value of the radical equal to **1.** Thus, formulas **(65′)** and **(65″)** take the forms

$$\sin(\alpha + \beta) = \sin\alpha\cos\beta + \sin\beta\cos\alpha, \tag{67}$$

$$\sinh(\alpha + \beta) = \sinh\alpha\cosh\beta + \sinh\beta\cosh\alpha. \tag{68}$$

From these and from formula **(66)**, we derive the addition theorems for the circular and hyperbolic cosines. Specifically,

$$\cos(\alpha + \beta) = \sqrt{1 - \sin^2(\alpha + \beta)} =$$
$$= \sqrt{(\sin^2\alpha + \cos^2\alpha)(\sin^2\beta + \cos^2\beta) - (\sin\alpha\cos\beta + \cos\alpha\sin\beta)^2} =$$
$$= \sqrt{\sin^2\alpha\sin^2\beta - 2\sin\alpha\sin\beta\cos\alpha\cos\beta + \cos^2\alpha\cos^2\beta} =$$
$$= \pm(\sin\alpha\sin\beta - \cos\alpha\cos\beta).$$

To choose the proper sign, we need in this case only to set $\beta = 0$. We see that we need to take the minus sign on the right:

$$\cos(\alpha + \beta) = \cos\alpha\cos\beta - \sin\alpha\sin\beta. \tag{69}$$

Analogously, for $\cosh(\alpha+\beta)$, we obtain, to begin with, the formula

$$\cosh(\alpha+\beta) = \sqrt{1+\sinh^2(\alpha+\beta)} =$$

$$= \sqrt{(\cosh^2\alpha - \sinh^2\alpha)(\cosh^2\beta - \sinh^2\beta) + (\sinh\alpha\cosh\beta + \cosh\alpha\sinh\beta)^2} =$$

$$= \sqrt{\cosh^2\alpha\cosh^2\beta + 2\cosh\alpha\cosh\beta\sinh\alpha\sinh\beta + \sinh^2\alpha\sinh^2\beta} =$$

$$= \pm(\cosh\alpha\cosh\beta + \sinh\alpha\sinh\beta).$$

For $\beta = 0$, we obtain $\cosh\alpha$ on the left and $\pm\cosh$ on the right. Therefore, on the right, we need to choose the plus sign:

$$\cosh(\alpha+\beta) = \cosh\alpha\cosh\beta + \sinh\alpha\sinh\beta. \tag{70}$$

Returning to formulas (66), let us replace t with it. We obtain

$$\left.\begin{aligned}\cos(it) &= \sqrt{1-\sin^2(it)} = \sqrt{1+\sinh^2 t} = \cosh t, \\[2mm] \cosh(it) &= \sqrt{1+\sinh^2(it)} = \sqrt{1-\sin^2 t} = \cosh t.\end{aligned}\right\} \tag{71}$$

(In the right-hand members, we choose the plus sign since, for $t = 0$, the values of both circular and hyperbolic cosines are 1.)

If follows from formula (66) that both cosines are even functions:

$$\cos(-t) = \sqrt{1-\sin^2 t} = \cos t, \quad \cosh(-t) = \sqrt{1+\sinh^2 t} = \cosh t. \tag{72}$$

From the addition theorem (67), we also conclude that the formula $\cos t = \sin(\pi/2 - t)$ is valid for all complex values of t. To see this, let us set $\alpha = \pi/2$ and $\beta = -t$ in (67). We obtain

$$\sin\left(\frac{\pi}{2} - t\right) = 1\cdot\cos(-t) + \sin(-t)\cdot 0 = \cos t. \tag{73}$$

Here, if we replace t with $\pi/2 - t$, we obtain

$$\cos\left(\frac{\pi}{2} - t\right) = \sin t. \tag{74}$$

Thus, formulas (5) of section 1 are valid (for all values of t both real and imaginary) if we define $\sin t$ as the function inverse to the integral

$$t = \int_0^w \frac{dz}{\sqrt{1 - z^2}},$$

and define $\cos t$ as the square root of $(1 - \sin^2 t)$ (with the convention that $\cos 0 = 1$). Since, under such a definition $\sin t$ is an odd function [see formulas (51)] and $\cos t$ is an even function [see formulas (72)], formulas (4) of section 1 also remain valid. But, as was shown in section 1, from formulas (4) and (5), we get all the "reduction" formulas of section 1, in particular, the periodicity of the circular functions. Therefore, in what follows, we shall use the formulas of section 1 for arbitrary complex values of t:

$$\cos\left(\frac{\pi}{2} + t\right) = -\sin t, \qquad \sin\left(\frac{\pi}{2} + t\right) = \cos t;$$

$$\cos(\pi - t) = -\cos t, \qquad \sin(\pi - t) = \sin t;$$

$$\cos(\pi + t) = -\cos t, \qquad \sin(\pi + t) = -\sin t;$$

$$\cos(2\pi + t) = \cos t, \qquad \sin(2\pi + t) = \sin t.$$

To summarize, we may say that the new definitions that we have made (beginning in Chapter 2) for $\sin t$ and $\cos t$ have led, for real values of t, to the functions that were defined on the entire real axis in section 1 on the basis of geometric considerations. We note that, for the hyperbolic functions $\sinh t$ and $\cosh t$, we do not need to go through the analogous proof. This is true because the difference between the cases of the circular and hyperbolic functions consists, with regard to the present matter, in the fact that $\sin t$, treated as a function of the real variable inverse to the integral

$$t = \int_0^y \frac{d\eta}{\sqrt{1 - \eta^2}},$$

was defined directly only on the finite interval $-\pi/2 \leqslant t \leqslant \pi/2$ and we had no information, to begin with, regarding its behavior outside that interval. The hyperbolic sine, on the other hand, treated as the inverse of the integral

$$t = \int_0^y \frac{d\eta}{\sqrt{1 + \eta^2}},$$

was defined from the very beginning on the entire real axis (see Chapter 2).

If we set $\alpha = \sigma$ and $\beta = i\tau$ in formulas (67)-(70), where σ and τ are real numbers, and use (52), (53), and (71), we obtain

$$
\begin{aligned}
\sin(\sigma + i\tau) &= \sin\sigma\,\cosh\tau + i\sinh\tau\cdot\cos\sigma, \\
\cos(\sigma + i\tau) &= \cos\sigma\,\cosh\tau - i\sin\sigma\cdot\sinh\tau, \\
\sinh(\sigma + i\tau) &= \sinh\sigma\,\cos\tau + i\sin\tau\cdot\cosh\sigma, \\
\cosh(\sigma + i\tau) &= \cosh\sigma\,\cos\tau + i\sinh\sigma\cdot\sin\tau.
\end{aligned}
\tag{75}
$$

These formulas express the circular and hyperbolic functions for an arbitrary complex value of the argument $t = \sigma + i\tau$ in terms of these functions of the real variables σ and τ.

23. In section 8, we derived expressions for $\cosh t$ and $\sinh t$ for real t in terms of the exponential function:

$$
\cosh t = \frac{e^t + e^{-t}}{2}, \quad \sinh t = \frac{e^t - e^{-t}}{2} .
$$

From this it follows that

$$
e^t = \cosh t + \sinh t .
\tag{76}
$$

Since we defined $\cosh t$ and $\sinh t$ above the arbitrary complex $t = \sigma + i\tau$, formula (76) enables us to define the exponential function for an arbitrary complex value of t. Using this definition, we obtain, with the aid of formulas (75),

$$
e^{\sigma + i\tau} = \cosh(\sigma + i\tau) + i\,\mathrm{sh}(\sigma + i\tau) =
$$

$$
= \cos\tau(\cosh\sigma + \sinh\sigma) + i\sin\tau(\cosh\sigma + \sinh\sigma).
$$

Now $\cosh\sigma + \sinh\sigma = e^\sigma$ in accordance with formula (76). Therefore,

$$
e^t = e^{\sigma + i\tau} = e^\sigma(\cos\tau + i\sin\tau).
\tag{77}
$$

If we replace t with it' in (76), we obtain

$$
e^{it'} = \cosh(it') + \sinh(it') = \cos t' + i\sin t',
$$

or, omitting the primes,

$$
e^{it} = \cos t + i\sin t.
\tag{78}
$$

This formula is due to Euler. Here, if we replace t with $-t$, we obtain

$$e^{-it} = \cos t - i \sin t. \tag{79}$$

From (78) and (79), we derive two other formulas of Euler:

$$\cos t = \frac{e^{it} + e^{-it}}{2}, \quad \sin t = \frac{e^{it} - e^{-it}}{2i}. \tag{80}$$

Let us verify that the addition theorem

$$e^{\alpha+\beta} = e^{\alpha} \cdot e^{\beta}, \tag{81}$$

where α and β are arbitrary complex numbers, holds for the exponential function e^t defined by formula (76). We have

$$e^{\alpha+\beta} = \cosh(\alpha + \beta) + \sinh(\alpha + \beta) =$$
$$= (\cosh\alpha \cdot \cosh\beta + \sinh\alpha \cdot \sinh\beta) + \sinh\alpha \cdot \cosh\beta + \sinh\beta \cdot \cosh\alpha =$$
$$= (\cosh\alpha + \sinh\alpha)(\cosh\beta + \sinh\beta) = e^{\alpha} \cdot e^{\beta}.$$

[Here, we used formulas (70), (68), and once again (76).] In particular, $1 = e^0 = e^{\alpha-\alpha} = e^{\alpha}e^{-\alpha}$. From this it follows that the value of e^{α} is always nonzero no matter what the value of the complex number α.

24. Let us turn to the lemniscate cosine cl t. In section 5, this function was defined for real values by the formula

$$\text{cl } t = \text{sl}\left(\frac{\omega}{2} - t\right). \tag{82}$$

Let us take (82) as the definition of cl t for arbitrary complex t. If we set $\alpha = \omega/2$ and $\beta = -t$ in (65''') and note that sl $\omega/2 = 1$ [formula (18')] and sl$(-t) = -$sl t [formula (51)], we obtain

$$\text{cl } t = \text{sl}\left(\frac{\omega}{2} - t\right) = \frac{\sqrt{1 - \text{sl}^4 t}}{1 + \text{sl}^2 t} = \sqrt{\frac{1 - \text{sl}^2 t}{1 + \text{sl}^2 t}}. \tag{83}$$

The value of the radical is chosen in such a way that cl $0 = 1$. Equation (83) can be written in the symmetric form

$$\text{sl}^2 t + \text{cl}^2 t + \text{sl}^2 t \cdot \text{cl}^2 t = 1. \tag{84}$$

From this, we get

$$\text{sl } t = \sqrt{\frac{1 - \text{cl}^2\, t}{1 + \text{cl}^2\, t}}.\tag{83'}$$

We note that, if we replace t with it, we obtain from (83) with the aid of (54)

$$\text{cl}\,(it) = \sqrt{\frac{1 - \text{sl}^2\,(it)}{1 + \text{sl}^2\,(it)}} = \sqrt{\frac{1 + \text{sl}^2\, t}{1 - \text{sl}^2\, t}} = \frac{1}{\text{cl}\, t}.\tag{85}$$

Furthermore, if we replace an arbitrary complex number t in (83) with $-t$, we get, by virtue of (51),

$$\text{cl}\,(-t) = \sqrt{\frac{1 - \text{sl}^2\,(-t)}{1 + \text{sl}^2\,(-t)}} = \sqrt{\frac{1 - \text{sl}^2\, t}{1 + \text{sl}^2\, t}} = \text{cl}\, t.\tag{86}$$

Thus, cl t is an even function. With the aid of (83), the expressions (65''') take the form

$$\text{sl}\,(\alpha + \beta) = \frac{\text{sl }\alpha\,\text{cl }\beta\,(1 + \text{sl}^2\,\beta) + \text{sl }\beta\,\text{cl }\alpha\,(1 + \text{sl}^2\,\alpha)}{1 + \text{sl}^2\,\alpha\,\text{sl}^2\,\beta} =$$
$$= \frac{\text{sl}^2\,\alpha - \text{sl}^2\,\beta}{\text{sl }\alpha\,\text{cl }\beta\,(1 + \text{sl}^2\,\beta) - \text{sl }\beta\cdot\text{cl }\alpha\,(1 + \text{sl}^2\,\alpha)}.\tag{87}$$

To establish the addition theorem for the lemniscate cosine as simply as possible, let us first replace t in (82) with $\omega/2 - t$. We obtain

$$\text{cl}\left(\frac{\omega}{2} - t\right) = \text{sl }t.\tag{82'}$$

From (82), it follows that

$$\text{cl }(\alpha + \beta) = \text{sl}\left[\left(\frac{\omega}{2} - \alpha\right) - \beta\right] = \text{sl}\left[\left(\frac{\omega}{2} - \beta\right) - \alpha\right].$$

Let us replace α by $\omega/2 - \alpha$ and β by $-\beta$ in the first expressions (87) and let us replace α by $\omega/2 - \beta$ and β by $-\alpha$ in the second expression. If we then use formulas (82) and (82'), we obtain

$$\text{cl}\,(\alpha + \beta) = \frac{\text{cl }\alpha\,\text{cl }\beta\,(1 + \text{sl}^2\,\beta) - \text{sl }\alpha\,\text{sl }\beta\,(1 + \text{cl}^2\,\alpha)}{1 + \text{cl}^2\,\alpha\cdot\text{sl}^2\,\beta} =$$
$$= \frac{\text{cl}^2\,\beta - \text{sl}^2\,\alpha}{\text{cl }\alpha\,\text{cl }\beta\,(1 + \text{sl}^2\,\alpha) + \text{sl }\alpha\,\text{sl }\beta\,(1 + \text{cl}^2\,\beta)}.\tag{88}$$

In contrast with the expressions (87), these last fractions are not represented symmetrically with respect to α and β. However, the formulas are of course valid when we reverse the roles of α and β.

25. We have already noted that all the "reduction formulas" of the circular functions are consequences of formulas (4) expressing the evenness of the function $\cos t$ and the oddness of the function $\sin t$ and of formulas (5) expressing the equality of the values of $\cos t_1$ and $\sin t_2$ if $t_1 + t_2 = \pi/2$. The lemniscate formulas possess analogous properties: $\operatorname{cl} t$ is an even and $\operatorname{sl} t$ is an odd function [cf. formulas (86) and (51)]. Furthermore, the values of $\operatorname{cl} t_1$ and $\operatorname{sl} t_2$ are equal if $t_1 + t_2 = \omega/2$ [cf. formulas (82) and (82′)]. Therefore, the corresponding "reduction formulas" obtained by the natural substitution of sl for sin, cl for cos, and ω for π are valid:

$$\operatorname{cl}\left(\frac{\omega}{2}+t\right)=-\operatorname{sl} t, \qquad \operatorname{sl}\left(\frac{\omega}{2}+t\right)=\operatorname{cl} t;$$

$$\operatorname{cl}(\omega-t)=-\operatorname{cl} t, \qquad \operatorname{sl}(\omega-t)=\operatorname{sl} t;$$

$$\operatorname{cl}(\omega+t)=-\operatorname{cl} t, \qquad \operatorname{sl}(\omega+t)=-\operatorname{sl} t;$$

$$\operatorname{cl}(2\omega+t)=\operatorname{cl} t, \qquad \operatorname{sl}(2\omega+t)=\operatorname{sl}(t).$$

It follows from this, in particular, that the lemniscate functions are periodic functions with period 2ω. Now we may assert that, for real values of t, the lemniscate functions defined by considering the inverse of the integral

$$t = \int_0^y \frac{d\eta}{\sqrt{1-\eta^4}},$$

on the entire real axis coincide with the lemniscate functions introduced in section 5 by way of a geometrical approach.

The identity (84) shows that, for real values of t, the values of the lemniscate functions

$$x = \operatorname{cl} t \text{ and } y = \operatorname{sl} t$$

can be regarded as the coordinates of a point A lying on the following fourth-order curve (see Fig. 19):

$$x^2 + y^2 + x^2 y^2 = 1. \tag{84'}$$

Together with the point A (x, y), let us consider the point A' (ξ, y), where $\xi = 1/x$. In accordance with (85) and (54), we have

$$\xi = \frac{1}{x} = \frac{1}{\mathrm{cl}\,t} = \mathrm{cl}\,(it), \quad y = \mathrm{sl}\,t = \frac{1}{i}\,\mathrm{sl}\,(it).$$

Obviously, ξ and y satisfy the equation obtained from (84′) by replacing x with $1/\xi$ but leaving y as it was:

$$\frac{1}{\xi^2} + y^2 + \frac{y^2}{\xi^2} = 1, \quad \text{or} \quad \xi^2 - y^2 - \xi^2 y^2 = 1. \tag{84″}$$

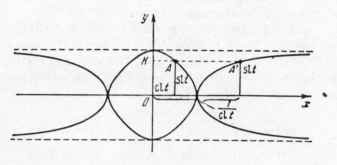

FIG. 19.

We have thus obtained a new fourth-order curve (one consisting of two unbounded branches as shown in Fig. 19). The coordinates of an arbitrary point A on it are expressed in terms of the values of the lemniscate functions of purely imaginary argument it:

$$\xi = \mathrm{cl}\,(it), \quad y = \frac{1}{i}\,\mathrm{sl}\,(it).$$

The variable t has an easy geometric interpretation. Specifically, from equations (84′) and (84″), we have

$$x = \frac{1 - y^2}{\sqrt{1 - y^4}}, \quad \xi = \frac{1 - y^2}{\sqrt{1 - y^4}}.$$

(For definiteness, all the points are taken with positive abscissa.) Therefore, for the areas of the curvilinear trapezoids $OCAK$ and $OCA'K$, we obtain

$$\text{area } OCAK = \int_0^y x\,dy = \int_0^y \frac{1 - \eta^2}{\sqrt{1 - \eta^4}}\,d\eta,$$

$$\text{area } OCA'K = \int_0^y \xi\,d\eta = \int_0^y \frac{1 + \eta^2}{\sqrt{1 - \eta^4}}\,d\eta.$$

from which we get

$$t = \int_0^y \frac{d\eta}{\sqrt{1-\eta^4}} = \frac{1}{2} \, [\text{area } OCAK + \text{area } OCA'K].$$

Such a geometric interpretation of t in this method of representing the lemniscate functions is valid both for the case of a real parameter t and a purely imaginary parameter it.

The addition theorems enable us to express the values of the lemniscate functions for an arbitrary complex variable $t = \sigma + i\tau$ in terms of the same functions of the real variable σ and τ. Specifically, when we set $\alpha = \sigma$ and $\beta = i\tau$ in the first of expressions (87) and use the formulas

$$\text{sl}\,(i\tau) = i\,\text{sl}\,\tau, \tag{54}$$

$$\text{cl}\,(i\tau) = \frac{1}{\text{cl}\,\tau}, \tag{85}$$

we obtain

$$\text{sl}\,(\sigma + i\tau) = \frac{\text{sl}\,\sigma\,(1 - \text{sl}^2\,\tau) + i\,\text{sl}\,\tau\,\text{cl}\,\sigma\,(1 + \text{sl}^2\,\sigma)}{1 - \text{sl}^2\,\sigma\,\,\text{sl}^2\,\tau}.$$

In this equation, let us replace $1 - \text{sl}^2\,\tau$ with $\text{cl}^2\,\tau\,(1 + \text{sl}^2\,\tau)$ in accordance with formula (84). After dividing through by $\text{cl}\,\tau$, we obtain

$$\text{sl}\,(\sigma + i\tau) = \frac{\text{sl}\,\sigma\,\text{cl}\,\tau\,(1 + \text{sl}^2\,\tau) + i\,\text{sl}\,\tau\,\text{cl}\,\sigma\,(1 + \text{sl}^2\,\sigma)}{1 - \text{sl}^2\,\sigma\,\text{sl}^2\,\tau}. \tag{89}$$

Analogously, the second of expressions (87) yields, for $\alpha = \sigma$ and $\beta = i\tau$,

$$\text{sl}\,(\sigma + i\tau) = \frac{\text{sl}^2\,\sigma + \text{sl}^2\,\tau}{\text{sl}\,\sigma\,\text{cl}\,\tau\,(1 + \text{sl}^2\,\tau) - i\,\text{sl}\,\tau\,\text{cl}\,\sigma\,(1 + \text{sl}^2\,\sigma)}. \tag{89'}$$

In a similar manner, we derive from formulas (88) the relation

$$\text{cl}\,(\sigma + i\tau) = \frac{\text{cl}\,\sigma\,\text{cl}\,\tau\,(1 + \text{sl}^2\,\tau) - i\,\text{sl}\,\sigma\,\text{sl}\,\tau\,(1 + \text{cl}^2\,\sigma)}{1 - \text{cl}^2\,\sigma\,\text{sl}^2\,\tau} =$$

$$= \frac{1 - \text{sl}^2\,\sigma\,\text{cl}^2\,\tau}{\text{cl}\,\sigma\,\text{cl}\,\tau\,(1 + \text{sl}^2\,\sigma) + i\,\text{sl}\,\sigma\,\text{sl}\,\tau\,(1 + \text{cl}^2\,\tau)}. \tag{90}$$

26. Let us now turn to the formulas for the Jacobian elliptic functions. The basic function $\operatorname{sn}(t, k)$ is used to define two other Jacobian elliptic functions:

$$\operatorname{cn}(t, k) = \sqrt{1 - \operatorname{sn}^2(t, k)}, \quad \operatorname{dn}(t, k) = \sqrt{1 - k^2 \operatorname{sn}^2(t, k)}. \tag{91}$$

Here, we take values of the radicals that assume the value 1 at $t = 0$, that is, at which $\operatorname{sn}(0, k) = 0$, and we extend the definition of these functions to the complex plane in such a way that continuity and differentiability are ensured. Thus,

$$\operatorname{cn}(0, k) = \operatorname{dn}(0, k) = 1.$$

The relations (91) can also be represented in the forms

$$\operatorname{sn}^2(t, k) + \operatorname{cn}^2(t, k) = 1, \quad k^2 \operatorname{sn}^2(t, k) + \operatorname{dn}^2(t, k) = 1 . \tag{91'}$$

It follows from formulas (91) that $\operatorname{cn}(t, k)$ and $\operatorname{dn}(t, k)$ are even functions

$$\operatorname{cn}(-t, k) = \operatorname{cn}(t, k), \quad \operatorname{dn}(-t, k) = \operatorname{dn}(t, k). \tag{92}$$

The notations for the Jacobian functions $\operatorname{sn} t$ and $\operatorname{cn} t$ underscore their similarity with the functions $\sin t$ and $\cos t$, respectively. If the modulus $k = 0$, these functions reduce to $\sin t$ and $\cos t$. The function $\operatorname{dn} t$ then reduces to the constant 1.

To see this, note that for $k = 0$, the integral

$$t = \int_0^w \frac{dz}{\sqrt{(1 - z^2)(1 - k^2 z^2)}}$$

becomes

$$t = \int_0^w \frac{dz}{\sqrt{1 - z^2}}.$$

Therefore, the inverse function $w = \operatorname{sn}(t, k)$ becomes $w = \sin t$. Formulas (91) yield

$$\operatorname{cn}(t, 0) = \cos t, \quad \operatorname{dn}(t, 0) = 1.$$

With the aid of formula (91), we can represent formula (55') in the form

$$\text{sn}\,(lt,\ k) = l\,\frac{\text{sn}\,(t,\ k')}{\text{cn}\,(t,\ k')}\,,\tag{93}$$

where $k' = \sqrt{1 - k^2}$ is the complementary modulus (with respect to k). Formulas (91) now enable us to express $\text{cn}\,(lt,\ k)$ and $\text{dn}\,(lt,\ k)$ in terms of the corresponding functions of the complementary modulus:

$$\text{cn}\,(it,\ k) = \sqrt{1 - \text{sn}^2\,(lt,\ k)} = \sqrt{1 + \frac{\text{sn}^2\,(t,\ k')}{\text{cn}^2\,(t,\ k')}} = \frac{1}{\text{cn}\,(t,\ k')};\tag{94}$$

$$\text{dn}\,(it,\ k) = \sqrt{1 - k^2\,\text{sn}^2\,(lt,\ k)} = \sqrt{1 + k^2\,\frac{\text{sn}^2\,(t,\ k')}{\text{cn}^2\,(t,\ k')}} =$$

$$= \frac{\sqrt{1 - \text{sn}^2\,(t,\ k') + (1 - k'^2)\,\text{sn}^2\,(t,\ k')}}{\text{cn}\,(t,\ k')} = \frac{\text{dn}\,(t,\ k')}{\text{cn}\,(t,\ k')}\,.\tag{95}$$

If in formulas (93)-(95), we replace t with lt (and hence it with $-t$), we obtain

$$\text{sn}\,(t,\ k) = -l\,\frac{\text{sn}\,(it,\ k')}{\text{cn}\,(it,\ k')}\,,$$

$$\text{cn}\,(t,\ k) = \frac{1}{\text{cn}\,(it,\ k')}\,,\quad \text{dn}\,(t,\ k) = \frac{\text{dn}\,(it,\ k')}{\text{cn}\,(it,\ k')}\,.$$

Noting that the complementary modulus k' vanishes for $k = 1$, we obtain, with the aid of formulas (52) and (71),

$$\text{sn}\,(t,\ 1) = -l\,\frac{\text{sn}\,(it,\ 0)}{\text{cn}\,(it,\ 0)} = -l\,\frac{\sin\,(it)}{\cos\,(it)} = \frac{\sinh t}{\cosh t}\,;$$

$$\text{cn}\,(t,\ 1) = \frac{1}{\text{cn}\,(it,\ 0)} = \frac{1}{\cos\,(it)} = \frac{1}{\cosh\,(t)}\,;$$

$$\text{dn}\,(t,\ 1) = \frac{\text{dn}\,(it,\ 0)}{\text{cn}\,(it,\ 0)} = \frac{1}{\cos\,(it)} = \frac{1}{\cosh t}\,.$$

Consequently, for $k = 1$, the Jacobian functions reduce to ratios of hyperbolic functions. The corresponding graphs (for real values of t) are shown in Figure 20. Thus, the Jacobian functions $\text{sn}\,(t,\ k)$, $\text{cn}\,(t,\ k)$, and $\text{dn}\,(t,\ k)$ for continuous variation in the modulus k from 0 to 1 form, as it were, a bridge from the circular functions $\sin t$ and $\cos t$ and also the function identically equal to the constant 1 to the hyperbolic functions: $(\sinh t)/\cosh t$, $1/\cosh t$, and $1/\cosh t$, respectively.

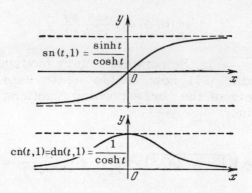

FIG. 20.

27. With the aid of the functions $\operatorname{cn}(t, k)$ and $\operatorname{dn}(t, k)$, the addition theorem (65^{IV}) for $\operatorname{sn}(t, k)$ takes the form

$$\operatorname{sn}(\alpha + \beta, k) =$$
$$= \frac{\operatorname{sn}(\alpha, k)\,\operatorname{cn}(\beta, k)\,\operatorname{dn}(\beta, k) + \operatorname{sn}(\beta, k)\,\operatorname{cn}(\alpha, k)\,\operatorname{dn}(\alpha, k)}{1 - k^2\,\operatorname{sn}^2(\alpha, k)\,\operatorname{sn}^2(\beta, k)} =$$
$$= \frac{\operatorname{sn}^2(\alpha, k) - \operatorname{sn}^2(\beta, k)}{\operatorname{sn}(\alpha, k)\,\operatorname{cn}(\beta, k)\,\operatorname{dn}(\beta, k) - \operatorname{sn}(\beta, k)\,\operatorname{cn}(\alpha, k)\,\operatorname{dn}(\alpha, k)}. \tag{96}$$

To derive addition theorems for $\operatorname{cn}(t, k)$ and $\operatorname{dn}(t, k)$ from (96), let us use the following identities, the validity of which can be checked by use of formulas (91'):

$$(\operatorname{sn}\alpha\,\operatorname{cn}\beta\,\operatorname{dn}\beta + \operatorname{sn}\beta\,\operatorname{cn}\alpha\,\operatorname{dn}\alpha)^2 +$$
$$+ (\operatorname{cn}\alpha\,\operatorname{cn}\beta - \operatorname{sn}\alpha\,\operatorname{sn}\beta\,\operatorname{dn}\alpha\,\operatorname{dn}\beta)^2 =$$
$$= (\operatorname{dn}\alpha\,\operatorname{dn}\beta - k^2\,\operatorname{sn}\alpha\,\operatorname{sn}\beta\,\operatorname{cn}\alpha\,\operatorname{cn}\beta)^2 +$$
$$+ k^2(\operatorname{sn}\alpha\,\operatorname{cn}\beta\,\operatorname{dn}\beta + \operatorname{sn}\beta\,\operatorname{cn}\alpha\,\operatorname{dn}\alpha)^2 = (1 - k^2\,\operatorname{sn}^2\alpha\,\operatorname{sn}^2\beta)^2.$$

We obtain

$$\operatorname{cn}(\alpha + \beta, k) = \sqrt{1 - \operatorname{sn}^2(\alpha + \beta, k)} =$$
$$= \frac{\sqrt{(1 - k^2\,\operatorname{sn}^2\alpha\,\operatorname{sn}^2\beta)^2 - (\operatorname{sn}\alpha\,\operatorname{cn}\beta\,\operatorname{dn}\beta + \operatorname{sn}\beta\,\operatorname{cn}\alpha\,\operatorname{dn}\alpha)^2}}{1 - k^2\,\operatorname{sn}^2\alpha\,\operatorname{sn}^2\beta} =$$
$$= \frac{\operatorname{cn}\alpha\,\operatorname{cn}\beta - \operatorname{sn}\alpha\,\operatorname{sn}\beta\,\operatorname{dn}\alpha\,\operatorname{dn}\beta}{1 - k^2\,\operatorname{sn}^2\alpha\,\operatorname{sn}^2\beta}; \tag{97}$$

$$\operatorname{dn}(\alpha + \beta, k) = \sqrt{1 - k^2\,\operatorname{sn}^2(\alpha + \beta, k)} =$$
$$= \frac{\sqrt{(1 - k^2\,\operatorname{sn}^2\alpha\,\operatorname{sn}^2\beta)^2 - k^2(\operatorname{sn}\alpha\,\operatorname{cn}\beta\,\operatorname{dn}\beta + \operatorname{sn}\beta\,\operatorname{cn}\alpha\,\operatorname{dn}\alpha)^2}}{1 - k^2\,\operatorname{sn}^2\alpha\,\operatorname{sn}^2\beta} =$$
$$= \frac{\operatorname{dn}\alpha\,\operatorname{dn}\beta - k^2\,\operatorname{sn}\alpha\,\operatorname{sn}\beta\,\operatorname{cn}\alpha\,\operatorname{cn}\beta}{1 - k^2\,\operatorname{sn}^2\alpha\,\operatorname{sn}^2\beta}. \tag{98}$$

These addition theorems enable us to express the values of the Jacobian elliptic functions for an arbitrary complex number $t = \sigma + i\tau$ in terms of the same functions of the real variables σ and τ. Here, we also need formulas (93), (94), and (95). The first of equations (96) yields

$$\text{sn}\,(\sigma + i\tau,\ k) =$$

$$= \frac{\text{sn}\,(\sigma,\ k)\,\text{cn}\,(i\tau,\ k)\,\text{dn}\,(i\tau,\ k) + \text{sn}\,(i\tau,\ k)\,\text{cn}\,(\sigma,\ k)\,\text{dn}\,(\sigma,\ k)}{1 - k^2\,\text{sn}^2\,(\sigma,\ k)\,\text{sn}^2\,(i\tau,\ k)} =$$

$$= \frac{\text{sn}\,(\sigma,\ k)\,\text{dn}\,(\tau,\ k') + i\,\text{sn}\,(\tau,\ k')\,\text{cn}\,(\tau,\ k')\,\text{cn}\,(\sigma,\ k)\,\text{dn}\,(\sigma,\ k)}{\text{cn}^2\,(\tau,\ k') + k^2\,\text{sn}^2\,(\sigma,\ k)\,\text{sn}^2\,(\tau,\ k')}, \qquad (99)$$

where $k' = \sqrt{1 - k^2}$. The second of expressions (96) enables us to represent the same result in a different form:

$$\text{sn}\,(\sigma + i\tau,\ k) =$$

$$= \frac{\text{sn}^2\,(\sigma,\ k)\,\text{cn}^2\,(\tau,\ k') + \text{sn}^2\,(\tau,\ k')}{\text{sn}\,(\sigma,\ k)\,\text{dn}\,(\tau,\ k') - i\,\text{sn}\,(\tau,\ k')\,\text{cn}\,(\tau,\ k')\,\text{cn}\,(\sigma,\ k)\,\text{dn}\,(\sigma,\ k)}. \qquad (99')$$

In the same way, by using formula (97), we see that

$$\text{cn}\,(\sigma + i\tau,\ k) =$$

$$= \frac{\text{cn}\,(\sigma,\ k)\,\text{cn}\,(\tau,\ k') - i\,\text{sn}\,(\sigma,\ k')\,\text{sn}\,(\tau,\ k')\,\text{dn}\,(\sigma,\ k)\,\text{dn}\,(\tau,\ k')}{\text{cn}^2\,(\tau,\ k') + k^2\,\text{sn}^2\,(\sigma,\ k)\,\text{sn}^2\,(\tau,\ k')}. \qquad (100)$$

The reader can use formula (91) to verify that the same result can be represented in the form

$$\text{cn}\,(\sigma + i\tau,\ k) =$$

$$= \frac{\text{cn}^2\,(\sigma,\ k) + k'^2\,\text{sn}^2\,(\sigma,\ k)\,\text{sn}^2\,(\tau,\ k')}{\text{cn}\,(\sigma,\ k)\,\text{cn}\,(\tau,\ k') + i\,\text{sn}\,(\sigma,\ k)\,\text{sn}\,(\tau,\ k')\,\text{dn}\,(\sigma,\ k)\,\text{dn}\,(\tau,\ k')}. \qquad (100')$$

Analogously, for the function dn t, we obtain

$$\text{dn}\,(\sigma + i\tau,\ k) =$$

$$= \frac{\text{dn}\,(\sigma,\ k)\,\text{cn}\,(\tau,\ k')\,\text{dn}\,(\tau,\ k') - ik^2\,\text{sn}\,(\sigma,\ k)\,\text{cn}\,(\sigma,\ k)\,\text{sn}\,(t,\ k')}{\text{cn}^2\,(\tau,\ k') + k^2\,\text{sn}^2\,(\sigma,\ k)\,\text{sn}^2\,(\tau,\ k')} =$$

$$= \frac{k^2\,\text{cn}^2\,(\sigma,\ k) + k'^2\,\text{cn}^2\,(\tau,\ k')}{\text{dn}\,(\sigma,\ k)\,\text{cn}\,(\tau,\ k')\,\text{dn}\,(\tau,\ k') + ik^2\,\text{sn}\,(\sigma,\ k)\,\text{cn}\,(\sigma,\ k)\,\text{sn}\,(\tau,\ k')}. \qquad (101)$$

28. Let us set

$$\int_0^1 \frac{dy}{\sqrt{(1 - y^2)\,(1 - k^2 y^2)}} = K\,(k) = K, \qquad (102)$$

where the integration is along the segment of the real axis between the points 0 and 1, so that $K(k)$ is a positive real number. It follows from (102) that

$$\text{sn}\,[K\,(k),\ k] = 1. \qquad (103)$$

Therefore,

$$\operatorname{cn}[K(k),\ k] = \sqrt{1 - \operatorname{sn}^2[K(k),\ k]} = 0$$

and

$$\operatorname{dn}[K(k),\ k] = \sqrt{1 - k^2 \operatorname{sn}^2[K(k),\ k]} = \sqrt{1 - k^2} = k' \cdot \tag{104}$$

For simplicity of writing, let us drop the symbol for the modulus k. If we then set $\alpha = K$ and $\beta = -t$ in formulas (96)-(98), we obtain

$$\operatorname{sn}(K - t) = \frac{\operatorname{sn} K \operatorname{cn} t \operatorname{dn} t - \operatorname{sn} t \operatorname{cn} K \operatorname{dn} K}{1 - k^2 \operatorname{sn}^2 K \operatorname{sn}^2 t} = \frac{\operatorname{cn} t \operatorname{dn} t}{1 - k^2 \operatorname{sn}^2 t} = \frac{\operatorname{cn} t}{\operatorname{dn} t}; \tag{105}$$

$$\operatorname{cn}(K - t) = \frac{\operatorname{cn} K \operatorname{cn} t + \operatorname{sn} K \operatorname{sn} t \operatorname{dn} K \operatorname{dn} t}{1 - k^2 \operatorname{sn}^2 K \operatorname{sn}^2 t} =$$

$$= \frac{k' \operatorname{sn} t \operatorname{dn} t}{1 - k^2 \operatorname{sn}^2 t} = k' \frac{\operatorname{sn} t}{\operatorname{dn} t}; \tag{106}$$

$$\operatorname{dn}(K - t) = \frac{\operatorname{dn} K \operatorname{dn} t + k^2 \operatorname{sn} K \operatorname{sn} t \operatorname{cn} K \operatorname{cn} t}{1 - k^2 \operatorname{sn}^2 K \operatorname{sn}^2 t} = \frac{k' \operatorname{dn} t}{1 - k^2 \operatorname{sn}^2 t} = \frac{k'}{\operatorname{dn} t}. \tag{107}$$

If we now replace t by $-t$, we obtain

$$\left.\begin{aligned}
\operatorname{sn}(K + t) &= \frac{\operatorname{cn} t}{\operatorname{dn} t} = \operatorname{sn}(K - t); \\[4pt]
\operatorname{cn}(K + t) &= -k' \frac{\operatorname{sn} t}{\operatorname{dn} t} = -\operatorname{cn}(K - t); \\[4pt]
\operatorname{dn}(K + t) &= \frac{k'}{\operatorname{dn} t} = \operatorname{dn}(K - t).
\end{aligned}\right\} \tag{108}$$

In the theory of Jacobian elliptic functions, formulas (105)-(108) play a role analogous to the reduction formulas in trigonometry.

If we replace t by $t + K$ in formulas (108), we find further "reduction formulas":

$$\left.\begin{aligned}
\operatorname{sn}(t + 2K) &= -\operatorname{sn} t, \\
\operatorname{cn}(t + 2K) &= -\operatorname{cn} t, \\
\operatorname{dn}(t + 2K) &= \operatorname{dn} t.
\end{aligned}\right\} \tag{109}$$

From the last formula, it follows that the function $\operatorname{dn} t$ is periodic with period $2K$. Finally, in the first two of formulas (109), let us replace t by $t + 2K$. This gives us

$$\operatorname{sn}(t + 4K) = \operatorname{sn} t, \qquad \operatorname{cn}(t + 4K) = \operatorname{cn} t. \tag{110}$$

Consequently, sn t and cn t are also periodic functions—in their cases, with period $4K$.

29. The formulas of the preceding section enable us to characterize completely the behavior of the Jacobian functions of a real variable without any other calculation. Let us begin with the function $y = \text{sn}(t, k)$ (for $0 < k < 1$). From the definition of this function, specifically, as the function inverse to the integral

$$t = \int\limits_0^y \frac{d\eta}{\sqrt{(1-\eta^2)(1-k^2\eta^2)}},$$

it follows that it increases monotonically from 0 to 1 as t increases from 0 to

$$K(k) = \int\limits_0^1 \frac{d\eta}{\sqrt{(1-\eta^2)(1-k^2\eta^2)}}$$

(cf. section 11). The first of formulas (108) shows that the graph $y = \text{sn}(t, k)$ is symmetric about the straight line $t = K$ and hence has the shape of a half-wave in the interval $0 \leqslant t \leqslant 2K$ (see Fig. 21a). Furthermore, if we replace t by $-t$ in the first of formulas (109), we get

$$\text{sn}(2K - t) = -\text{sn}(-t) = \text{sn}\, t.$$

By comparing $\text{sn}(2K + t)$ with $\text{sn}(2K - t)$, we obtain

$$\text{sn}(2K + t) = -\text{sn}(2K - t).$$

This means that the graph of $y = \text{sn}(t, k)$ is symmetric about the point $(2K, 0)$. Consequently, in the interval $0 \leqslant t \leqslant 4K$, it has the same shape as does a sine wave in the interval $0 \leqslant t \leqslant 2\pi$ (see Fig. 21a). Since we know that the function $\text{sn}(t, k)$ is periodic with period $4K$, we can now proceed to construct its graph.

To determine the nature of the graph of the function $y = \text{cn}(t, k)$, we can begin with the relation $\text{cn}(t, k) = \sqrt{1 - \text{sn}^2(t, k)}$, from which it follows that this function decreases monotonically from 1 to 0 in the interval $0 \leqslant t \leqslant K$. Furthermore, the graph is constructed just as above, by use of formulas (108)-(110). We see that this graph looks much like that of the cosine (see Fig. 21b).

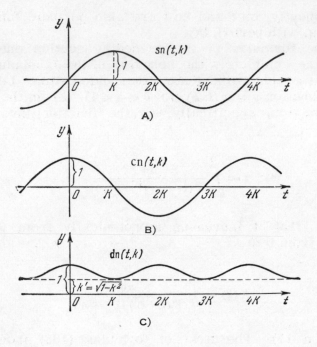

FIG. 21.

In an analogous manner, we obtain the graph of the function $y = \mathrm{dn}\,(t,\ k)$. The formula

$$\mathrm{dn}\,(t,\ k) = \sqrt{1 - k^2 \, \mathrm{sn}^2\,(t,\ k)}$$

shows first that this function decreases from 1 to $\sqrt{1-k^2} = k'$ in the interval $0 \leqslant t \leqslant K$. The graph is then extended to the entire real axis by using the appropriate relations (108) and (109). It is shown in Figure 21c.

It follows from the above analysis that all real zeros of $\mathrm{sn}\,(t,\ k)$ [that is, the real roots of the equation $\mathrm{sn}\,(t,\ k) = 0$] are exhausted by points of the form $t = 2mK\,(k)$, where m is an arbitrary integer.

Analogously, the real zeros of $\mathrm{cn}\,(t,\ k)$ are of the form

$$t = (2m - 1)\,K\,(k).$$

The function $\mathrm{dn}\,(t,\ k)$ has no real zeros at all (if $0 < k < 1$).

30. Let us show that the generalized sine $s(t)$ can in all cases be represented in terms of the functions $\sin t$ and $\sinh t$ or in terms of the Jacobian functions. Specifically, let us show that, for $n = 0$ (where n is the coefficient of z^4 in the expression

$1 + mz^2 + nz^4$), it can be expressed in terms of $\sin t$ or $\sinh t$ and that, for $n \neq 0$, it can be expressed in terms of the Jacobian functions.

If $n = 0$ and $m \neq 0$, then $1 + mz^2$ can be written in the form $1 \pm \lambda^2 z^2$, where $\lambda > 0$. Then, if we represent the relation $w = s(t)$ in the form

$$t = \int_0^w \frac{dz}{\sqrt{1 \pm \lambda^2 z^2}},$$

and make the change of variable $\zeta = \lambda z$, we obtain

$$t = \frac{1}{\lambda} \int_0^{\lambda w} \frac{d\zeta}{\sqrt{1 \pm \zeta^2}}.$$

From this we have either $\lambda w = \sin(\lambda t)$ or $\lambda w = \sinh(\lambda t)$. Thus, in the case in question,

$$s(t) = \frac{1}{\lambda} \sin(\lambda t), \quad \text{or} \quad s(t) = \frac{1}{\lambda} \sinh(\lambda, t). \tag{111}$$

Suppose now that $n \neq 0$ and, as always, that $m^2 - 4n \neq 0$. We have two cases:

CASE I. $m^2 - 4n > 0$. Here, the roots x_1 and x_2 of the equation

$$x^2 + mx + n = 0$$

are real and distinct. We have

$$x^2 + mx + n = (x - x_1)(x - x_2),$$

or, if we replace x with $1/z^2$,

$$1 + mz^2 + nz^4 = (1 - x_1 z^2)(1 - x_2 z^2).$$

At this point we need to consider three subcases: (a) x_1 and x_2 both positive, (b) x_1 and x_2 of opposite sign, (c) x_1 and x_2 both negative.

Subcase (a): We can assume that x_1 and x_2 have the values λ^2 and μ^2, where $\lambda > \mu > 0$. Then,

$$1 + mz^2 + nz^4 = (1 - \lambda^2 z^2)(1 - \mu^2 z^2).$$

Consequently, the equation $w = s(t)$ takes the form

$$t = \int_0^w \frac{dz}{\sqrt{(1 - \lambda^2 z^2)(1 - \mu^2 z^2)}}.$$

If we make the change of variable $\zeta = \lambda z$, we obtain

$$t = \frac{1}{\lambda} \int_0^{\lambda w} \frac{d\zeta}{\sqrt{(1 - \zeta^2)(1 - k^2 \zeta^2)}}, \text{where } 0 < k = \frac{\mu}{\lambda} < 1.$$

Thus, in this subcase,

$$w = s(t) = \frac{1}{\lambda} \operatorname{sn}(\lambda t, \ k). \tag{112}$$

Subcase (b): We can assume that $x_1 = \lambda^2$ and $x_2 = -\mu^2$, where λ and μ are both positive. We obtain the following decomposition into factors:

$$1 + mz^2 + nz^4 = (1 - x_1 z^2)(1 - x_2 z^2) = (1 - \lambda^2 z^2)(1 + \mu^2 z^2).$$

If, in the integral

$$t = \int_0^w \frac{dz}{\sqrt{(1 - \lambda^2 z^2)(1 + \mu^2 z^2)}}$$

we make the change of variable $\zeta = \sqrt{1 - \lambda^2 z^2}$, we obtain

$$t = -\frac{1}{\sqrt{\lambda^2 + \mu^2}} \int_1^{\sqrt{1 - \lambda^2 w^2}} \frac{d\zeta}{\sqrt{(1 - \zeta^2)(1 - k^2 \zeta^2)}},$$

where

$$0 < k = \frac{\mu}{\sqrt{\lambda^2 + \mu^2}} < 1.$$

If we set

$$\int_0^1 \frac{d\zeta}{\sqrt{(1 - \zeta^2)(1 - k^2 \zeta^2)}} = K,$$

we obtain

$$K - \sqrt{\lambda^2 + \mu^2}\, t = \int_0^{\sqrt{1-\lambda^2 w^2}} \frac{d\zeta}{\sqrt{(1 - \zeta^2)(1 - k^2 \zeta^2)}}$$

or

$$\sqrt{1 - \lambda^2 w^2} = \mathrm{sn}\left(K - \sqrt{\lambda^2 + \mu^2}\, t,\ k\right) =$$
$$= \frac{\mathrm{cn}\,(\sqrt{\lambda^2 + \mu^2}\, t,\ k)}{\mathrm{dn}\,(\sqrt{\lambda^2 + \mu^2}\, t,\ k)} \qquad \text{[cf. (105)]}$$

in subcase (b), so that

$$w = s(t) = \frac{1}{\lambda} \sqrt{1 - \frac{\mathrm{cn}^2\,(\sqrt{\lambda^2 + \mu^2}\, t,\ k)}{\mathrm{dn}^2\,(\sqrt{\lambda^2 + \mu^2}\, t,\ k)}} = \frac{k'}{\lambda}\, \frac{\mathrm{sn}\,(\sqrt{\lambda^2 + \mu^2}\, t,\ k)}{\mathrm{dn}\,(\sqrt{\lambda^2 + \mu^2}\, t,\ k)}.$$

Noting that, in the present case,

$$k' = \sqrt{1 - k^2} = \frac{\lambda}{\sqrt{\lambda^2 + \mu^2}},$$

we can rewrite our last result in the form

$$w = s(t) = \frac{1}{\sqrt{\lambda^2 + \mu^2}}\, \frac{\mathrm{sn}\,(\sqrt{\lambda^2 + \mu^2}\, t,\ k)}{\mathrm{dn}\,(\sqrt{\lambda^2 + \mu^2}\, t,\ k)}. \qquad (113)$$

For $\lambda = \mu = 1$, the integral

$$\int_0^w \frac{dz}{\sqrt{(1 - \lambda^2 z^2)(1 + \mu^2 z^2)}}$$

coincides with

$$\int_0^w \frac{dz}{\sqrt{1 - z^4}}.$$

Therefore, $s(t) = \mathrm{sl}(t)$, and we obtain

$$\mathrm{sl}\, t = \frac{1}{\sqrt{2}}\, \frac{\mathrm{sn}\left(\sqrt{2}\, t,\ \dfrac{1}{\sqrt{2}}\right)}{\mathrm{dn}\left(\sqrt{2}\, t,\ \dfrac{1}{\sqrt{2}}\right)}. \qquad (113')$$

For cl t, we obtain

$$\operatorname{cl} t = \sqrt{\frac{1 - \operatorname{sl}^2 t}{1 + \operatorname{sl}^2 t}} = \sqrt{\frac{\operatorname{dn}^2\left(\sqrt{2}\,t,\, \frac{1}{\sqrt{2}}\right) - \frac{1}{2}\operatorname{sn}^2\left(\sqrt{2}\,t,\, \frac{1}{\sqrt{2}}\right)}{\operatorname{dn}^2\left(\sqrt{2}\,t\, \frac{1}{\sqrt{2}}\right) + \frac{1}{2}\operatorname{sn}^2\left(\sqrt{2}\,t,\, \frac{1}{\sqrt{2}}\right)}} =$$

$$= \operatorname{cn}\left(\sqrt{2}\,t,\, \frac{1}{\sqrt{2}}\right). \tag{113''}$$

Thus, the *lemniscate functions can be expressed in terms of the Jacobian functions with modulus* $1/\sqrt{2}$.

Subcase (c): When x_1 and x_2 are both negative, they can be represented in the forms $-\lambda^2$ and $-\mu^2$, and we can assume that $\lambda > \mu > 0$. Therefore,

$$1 + mz^2 + nz^4 = (1 - x_1 z^2)(1 - x_2 z^2) = (1 + \lambda^2 z^2)(1 + \mu^2 z^2).$$

In the integral

$$t = \int\limits_0^w \frac{dz}{\sqrt{(1 + \lambda^2 z^2)(1 + \mu^2 z^2)}}$$

we make the change of variable $\zeta = \lambda z/\sqrt{1 + \lambda^2 z^2}$ (cf. calculation in section 17, where $\lambda = 1$ and $\mu = k$). We then obtain

$$t = \frac{1}{\lambda} \int\limits_0^{\frac{\lambda w}{\sqrt{1 + \lambda^2 w^2}}} \frac{d\zeta}{\sqrt{(1 - \zeta^2)(1 - k^2 \zeta^2)}} \text{ where } 0 < k = \frac{\sqrt{\lambda^2 - \mu^2}}{\lambda} < 1.$$

From this, we get

$$\frac{\lambda w}{\sqrt{1 + \lambda^2 w^2}} = \operatorname{sn}(\lambda t,\, k),$$

or

$$w = s(t) = \frac{1}{\lambda}\frac{\operatorname{sn}(\lambda t, k)}{\sqrt{1 - \operatorname{sn}^2(\lambda t, k)}} = \frac{1}{\lambda}\frac{\operatorname{sn}(\lambda t, k)}{\operatorname{sn}(\lambda t, k)}. \tag{114}$$

It remains for us to consider

CASE II. $m^2 - 4n < 0$ (obviously, here $n > 0$). Since the roots x_1 and x_2 of the equation

$$x^2 + mx + n = 0$$

are imaginary, the roots of the equation

$$\xi^4 + m\xi^2 + n = 0,$$

defined by

$$\xi_1^2 = \xi_2^2 = x_1, \quad \xi_3^2 = \xi_4^2 = x_2,$$

are also imaginary. Furthermore, their real parts are nonzero (because otherwise the squares of the roots would be real numbers). Noting that ξ_1, ξ_2, ξ_3 and ξ_4 must also be pairwise conjugate and changing the numbering if necessary, we have

$$\xi_1 = -\xi_2 = \alpha + i\beta, \quad \xi_3 = -\xi_4 = \alpha - i\beta \quad (\alpha > 0, \beta > 0).$$

In the decomposition

$$\xi^4 + m\xi^2 + n = (\xi - \xi_1)(\xi - \xi_2)(\xi - \xi_3)(\xi - \xi_4)$$

let us replace ξ with $1/z$. We then obtain the following decomposition into factors:

$$1 + mz^2 + nz^4 =$$
$$= [1 + (\alpha + i\beta)z][1 + (\alpha - i\beta)z][1 - (\alpha + i\beta)z][1 - (\alpha - i\beta)z] =$$
$$= [1 + 2\alpha z + (\alpha^2 + \beta^2)z^2][1 - 2\alpha z + (\alpha^2 + \beta^2)z^2].$$

Obviously, $\alpha^2 + \beta^2 = \sqrt{n}$ (from which we get $0 < \alpha < \sqrt[4]{n}$). Consequently, our integral is of the form

$$t = \int_0^w \frac{dz}{\sqrt{(1 + 2\alpha z + \sqrt{n}\, z^2)(1 - 2\alpha z + \sqrt{n}\, z^2)}}.$$

Let us show that it reduces to one of the cases considered above when we make the substitution

$$z = \frac{1}{\sqrt[4]{n}} \cdot \frac{\zeta - 1}{\zeta + 1}.$$

When we make this substitution and perform some manipulations in the integral, we obtain

$$t = \int_{1}^{\frac{1+\sqrt[4]{n}\,w}{1-\sqrt[4]{n}\,w}} \frac{d\zeta}{\sqrt{\left[\left(\sqrt[4]{n}-\alpha\right)+\left(\sqrt[4]{n}+\alpha\right)\zeta^2\right]\left[\left(\sqrt[4]{n}+\alpha\right)+\left(\sqrt[4]{n}-\alpha\right)\zeta^2\right]}} =$$

$$= \frac{1}{\beta}\int_{1}^{\frac{1+\sqrt[4]{n}\,w}{1+\sqrt[4]{n}\,w}} \frac{d\zeta}{\sqrt{(1+\lambda^2\zeta^2)(1+\mu^2\zeta^2)}},$$

$$\lambda = \sqrt{\frac{\sqrt[4]{n}+\alpha}{\sqrt[4]{n}-\alpha}} > \mu = \sqrt{\frac{\sqrt[4]{n}-\alpha}{\sqrt[4]{n}+\alpha}} > 0.$$

Let us set

$$\int_{0}^{1} \frac{d\zeta}{\sqrt{(1+\lambda^2\zeta^2)(1+\mu^2\zeta^2)}} = A.$$

Then,

$$\beta t + A = \int_{0}^{\frac{1+\sqrt[4]{n}\,w}{1-\sqrt[4]{n}\,w}} \frac{d\zeta}{\sqrt{(1+\lambda^2\zeta^2)(1+\mu^2\zeta^2)}}.$$

Thus, this brings us to Case I (c). Therefore, in accordance with formula (114),

$$\frac{1+\sqrt[4]{n}\,w}{1-\sqrt[4]{n}\,w} = \frac{1}{\lambda}\frac{\operatorname{sn}(\beta t + A,\,k)}{\operatorname{cn}(\beta t + A,\,k)},$$

where

$$k = \frac{\sqrt{\lambda^2 - \mu^2}}{\lambda}.$$

From this we get, finally,

$$w = s(t) = \frac{1}{\sqrt[4]{n}} \cdot \frac{\operatorname{sn}(\beta t + A,\,k) - \lambda \operatorname{cn}(\beta t + A,\,k)}{\operatorname{sn}(\beta t + A,\,k) + \lambda \operatorname{cn}(\beta t + A,\,k)}.$$

Thus, we have shown in this section that the generalized sine with $n \neq 0$ can be expressed in terms of the Jacobian functions with appropriate modulus k and, for $n = 0$, in terms of the circular or hyperbolic sine. All this will give us the right in what follows to confine ourselves to a study of only three sines (together with the corresponding cosines): the circular, trigonometric, and Jacobian (the sine amplitude). However, together with these, we shall also consider the lemniscate functions since it is for this special case that the properties of the Jacobian functions manifest themselves in the simplest manner.

Zeros and Poles.
Simple and Double Periodicity.
The Concept of an Elliptic Function

31. If we compare formulas (75), obtained above for circular and hyperbolic functions with formulas (89), (89′), and (90) for the lemniscate functions or with formulas (99)-(101) for the Jacobian functions, we see a sharp difference between formulas (75) and the other six. Specifically, the circular and hyperbolic functions are represented as polynomial functions of $\sin \sigma$, $\cos \sigma$, $\sinh \sigma$, and $\cosh \sigma$, whereas the lemniscate functions were represented as fractional expressions in terms of $\mathrm{sl}\,\sigma$, $\mathrm{cl}\,\sigma$, $\mathrm{sl}\,\tau$, and $\mathrm{cl}\,\tau$ and the Jacobian functions were expressed as fractional expressions in terms of the Jacobian functions of the real variables σ and τ.

Therefore, the functions $\sin t$, $\cos t$, $\sinh t$, and $\cosh t$ are defined and have finite values for every complex t. On the other hand, the functions $\mathrm{sl}\,t$, $\mathrm{cl}\,t$, $\mathrm{sn}(t, k)$, $\mathrm{cn}(t, k)$ and $\mathrm{dn}(t, k)$ are not defined for those values of t at which the denominator of the fraction in question vanishes.

Let us look into this phenomenon more closely, beginning with $\mathrm{sl}\,t$. The denominator of the fraction in formula (89) is equal to $1 - \mathrm{sl}^2\sigma \cdot \mathrm{sl}^2\tau$. It vanishes if and only if

$$\mathrm{sl}\,\sigma \cdot \mathrm{sl}\,\tau = \pm 1. \tag{115}$$

But $\mathrm{sl}\,\sigma$ and $\mathrm{sl}\,\tau$ are real numbers that do not exceed 1 in absolute value. (We recall from section 5 that $\mathrm{sl}\,\sigma$ is the signed length of the chord of the lemniscate.) Therefore, equation (115) is equivalent to the two equations

$$\text{sl } \sigma = \pm 1 \text{ and sl } \tau = \pm 1. \tag{116}$$

It follows from the same geometric representation of sl σ that the condition sl $\sigma = 1$ is equivalent to the condition $\sigma = \omega/2 + 2m\omega$, where m is an arbitrary integer (2ω being the period of sl σ). Since sl σ is an odd function, the condition $\sigma = -1$ is equivalent to the condition $\sigma = -\omega/2 + 2m\omega$. Thus, the denominator of the fraction (89) vanishes at all points with coordinates

$$\sigma = \pm \frac{\omega}{2} + 2m\omega, \quad \tau = \pm \frac{\omega}{2} + 2n\omega$$

$$(m = 0, \ \pm 1, \ \pm 2, \ \ldots; \ n = 0, \ \pm 1, \ \pm 2, \ \ldots)$$

and only at such points.

The corresponding complex numbers $t = \sigma + i\tau$ are exhausted by the formula

$$t = (4m \pm 1)\frac{\omega}{2} + (4n \pm 1)\frac{\omega i}{2}.$$

But if m ranges over all integers $0, \pm 1, \pm 2, \pm 3, \ldots$, the quantity $4m \pm 1$ assumes all odd values $\pm 1, \pm 3, \pm 5, \ldots$.

Therefore, the values of t can finally be represented in the form

$$t = (2p - 1)\frac{\omega}{2} + (2q - 1)\frac{\omega i}{2}, \tag{117}$$

where $p = 0, \pm 1, \pm 2, \ldots$ and $q = 0, \pm 1, \pm 2, \ldots$.

Let us look at one of these points. If $\sigma = (2p - 1)\omega/2$, then sl $\sigma = (-1)^{p-1}$, as can easily be derived from observations made above. Therefore, $\text{sl}^2 \sigma = 1$, and formula (83) yields cl $\sigma = 0$. Analogously, for $\tau = (2q - 1)\omega/2$, we have sl $\tau = (-1)^{q-1}$ and cl $\tau = 0$. If we substitute these values into the right-hand side of formula (89), not only the denominator but also the numerator in the formula will obviously vanish and we cannot draw any conclusion as to the behavior of sl t as $t \to (2p - 1)\omega/2 + (2q - 1)\omega i/2$ immediately. Formula (89') saves the situation. Here, the denominator of the fraction is equal to 0, just as before, but the numerator $\text{sl}^2 \sigma + \text{sl}^2 \tau = 2$ and thus is nonzero. From this it follows that sl t approaches ∞ as $t \to (2p - 1)\omega/2 + (2q - 1)\omega i/2$. (Here, we use the fact that the lemniscate functions of a real variable are continuous.) We can now extend the definition of sl t, to the entire complex plane by setting

$$\text{sl}\left[(2p-1)\frac{\omega}{2}+(2q-1)\frac{\omega i}{2}\right]=\infty,$$

$$p=0,\ \pm1,\ \pm2,\ \ldots;\ q=0,\ \pm1,\ \pm2,\ \ldots. \qquad (118)$$

If we refer to a point in the complex plane at which a function becomes infinite (that is, at which the function approaches ∞ as the argument approaches that point) as a pole of the function, we may now say that formula (118) provides all the infinitely many poles of the lemniscate sine.

Analogously, it would be possible to determine all the poles of the lemniscate cosine from formulas (90). However, it is simpler to start with formulas (82):

$$\text{cl}\ t=\text{sl}\left(\frac{\omega}{2}-t\right).$$

It follows from this formula that $\text{cl}\ t$ approaches ∞ as t approaches a point a if and only if $\text{sl}(\omega/2-t)$ approaches ∞ as $\omega/2-t$ approaches $\omega/2-a$. From this, we get, just as above,

$$\frac{\omega}{2}-a=(2p-1)\frac{\omega}{2}+(2q-1)\frac{\omega i}{2};$$

that is,

$$a=2(-p+1)\frac{\omega}{2}+[2(-q+1)-1]\frac{\omega i}{2}.$$

If we replace $-p+1$ in this equation with p' and if we replace $-q+1$ with q', we see that all the poles of $\text{cl}\ t$ are represented in the form

$$t=p'\omega+(2q'-1)\frac{\omega i}{2}, \qquad (119)$$

where p' and q' are any integers.

32. By an analogous procedure, we find the poles of the Jacobian functions. Let us begin with $\text{sn}(t,\ k)$ (where $0<k<1$). The denominator of formula (99) is of the form

$$\text{cn}^2(\tau,\ k')+k^2\text{sn}^2(\sigma,\ k)\text{sn}^2(\tau,\ k'). \qquad (120)$$

Since the values of the Jacobian functions are real when σ and τ are real, vanishing of this sum is equivalent to the two conditions

$$\text{cn}(\tau,\ k')=0,\quad \text{sn}(\sigma,\ k)\text{sn}(\tau,\ k')=0.$$

But if $\mathrm{cn}\,(\tau,\ k')=0$, then $\mathrm{sn}\,(\tau,\ k')=\pm 1$ [cf. (91)]. Therefore, we see that (120) vanishes if and only if the two equations

$$\mathrm{cn}\,(\tau,\ k')=0, \quad \mathrm{sn}\,(\sigma,\ k)=0 \tag{121}$$

hold simultaneously. From this it follows in accordance with section 29 that

$$\sigma = 2mK\,(k) \text{ and } \tau = (2n-1)\,K\,(k');$$

that is,

$$t = 2mK\,(k) + i\,(2n-1)\,K\,(k').$$

Denoting $K\,(k)$ by K and $K\,(k')$ by K', we rewrite these values in the form

$$t = 2mK + i\,(2n-1)\,K', \tag{122}$$

where m and n are any integers.

However, if we substitute the values that we have found for σ and τ into formula (99), we see that not only the denominator but also the numerator vanishes [since $\mathrm{sn}\,(\sigma,\ k)=\mathrm{cn}\,(\tau,k')=0$]. Therefore, this formula does not enable us to draw any conclusions immediately regarding the behavior of $\mathrm{sn}\,(t,\ k)$ as $t \to 2mK + (2n-1)\,iK'$. Formula (99') comes to our aid. Since $\mathrm{sn}\,(\tau,\ k')=\pm 1$ when $\mathrm{cn}\,(\tau,\ k')=0$ [by the first of formulas (91)], we have $\mathrm{sn}^2\,(\tau,\ k')=1$, and formula (99') shows that $\mathrm{sn}\,(t,\ k) \to \infty$ as t approaches any of the points (122). Consequently, the values found for t represent the poles (all of them) of the Jacobian function $\mathrm{sn}\,(t,\ k)$.

By an analogous procedure, we can see that the values (122) constitute all the poles of the functions $\mathrm{cn}\,(t,\ k)$ and $\mathrm{dn}\,(t,\ k)$. Furthermore, the fact that the poles of these functions must coincide with the poles of $\mathrm{sn}\,(t,\ k)$ follows from identities (91).

33. In what follows, we shall also need to know the zeros of the functions that we are studying, that is, all the points in the complex plane at which the functions vanish. Let us begin with the circular sine. From the first of formulas (75), we have

$$\sin t = \sin\,(\sigma + i\tau) = \sin\sigma\cosh\tau + i\sinh\tau\cos\sigma. \tag{75'}$$

From this it follows that the equation

$$\sin t = 0 \tag{123}$$

is equivalent to the system of equations

$$\sin \sigma \cdot \cosh \tau = 0,$$
$$\sinh \tau \cdot \cos \sigma = 0. \tag{124}$$

Let us look at the first of equations (124). Since $\cosh \tau \neq 0$ (recall the geometric representation of $\cosh \tau$ in section 2 or formula (32): $\cosh t = e^t + e^{-t})/2$), we conclude that $\sin \sigma = 0$. Therefore, $\sigma = m\pi$, where $m = 0, \pm 1, \pm 2, \ldots$. Consequently, $\cos \sigma = (-1)^m \neq 0$. The second of equations (124) yields $\sinh \tau = 0$, so that $\tau = 0$. (Recall the geometric representation of $\sinh \tau$ in section 2). Formula (31) leads to the same conclusion. Thus,

$$t = \sigma + i\tau = m\pi, \quad m = 0, \pm 1, \pm 2, \ldots . \tag{125}$$

This expression takes care of all the zeros of $\sin t$. We see that none of them is imaginary. Extension of the definition of the circular sine to the complex plane does not yield any new zeros.

We leave it as an exercise for the reader to use the second of formulas (75) to show that all the zeros of $\cos t$ are represented by the expression

$$t = \sigma + i\tau = (2m - 1)\frac{\pi}{2}, \quad m = 0, \pm 1, \pm 2, \ldots . \tag{126}$$

Finally, by the same procedure, we can find the zeros of the hyperbolic functions. However, it is simpler to achieve this end by using the relations

$$\sin (it) = i \sinh t, \qquad \cos (it) = \cosh t .$$

It follows from the first of these that the equation $\sinh t = 0$ is equivalent to the equation $\sin (it) = 0$. Therefore, $it = m\pi$ and hence

$$t = (- m) \pi i = n\pi i,$$

where n is also an arbitrary integer. In just the same way, we can show that the zeros of $\cosh t$ are given by the formula

$$t = (2n - 1)\frac{\pi i}{2} ,$$

where n is an arbitrary integer.

34. Let us now seek the zeros of the lemniscate sine. Using formula (89′), we conclude that the equation $\mathrm{sl}\, t = \mathrm{sl}\,(\sigma + i\tau) = 0$ implies that $\mathrm{sl}^2\,\sigma + \mathrm{sl}^2\,\tau = 0$. Thus, we obtain the two equations

$$\left.\begin{aligned} \mathrm{sl}\,\sigma &= 0, \\ \mathrm{sl}\,\tau &= 0. \end{aligned}\right\} \tag{127}$$

From this we get $\sigma = m\omega$, $\tau = n\omega$ (where m and n are arbitrary integers). Consequently,

$$t = m\omega + n\omega i, \quad m = 0, \ \pm 1, \ \pm 2, \ \ldots; \quad n = 0, \ \pm 1, \ \pm 2, \ \ldots. \tag{128}$$

However, for $\mathrm{sl}\,\sigma = 0$ and $\mathrm{sl}\,\tau = 0$, the denominator of the fraction (89′) vanishes. Therefore, formula (89′) does not tell us the values of $\mathrm{sl}\, t$ at the points that we have found. Let us turn to formula (89) for $\mathrm{sl}\,(\sigma + i\tau)$. Here, the numerator of the fraction is equal to 0 when equations (127) are satisfied but the denominator is equal to 1. Therefore, $\mathrm{sl}\,(m\omega + n\omega i) = 0$ and, hence, formula (128) does indeed give the zeros of $\mathrm{sl}\, t$ [all of them since formula (89′) implies that the conditions found are necessary for vanishing of $\mathrm{sl}\, t$].

To find the zeros of $\mathrm{cl}\, t$, the simplest procedure is to use formula (82):

$$\mathrm{cl}\, t = \mathrm{sl}\left(\frac{\omega}{2} - t\right).$$

From this formula, it follows that equation $\mathrm{cl}\, t = 0$ is equivalent to the equation $\mathrm{sl}\,(\omega/2 - t) = 0$. Therefore, $\omega/2 - t = m\omega + n\omega i$. From this we get

$$t = [2(-m + 1) - 1]\frac{\omega}{2} + (-n)\omega i = (2m' - 1)\frac{\omega}{2} + n'\omega i, \tag{129}$$

where m' and n' are arbitrary integers. Formula (129) provides all the zeros of $\mathrm{cl}\, t$.

35. Formula (99′) is convenient for finding the zeros of $\mathrm{sn}\,(t, k)$. From this formula, we see that a necessary condition for $\mathrm{sn}\,(\sigma + i\tau, k)$ to vanish is

$$\mathrm{sn}^2(\sigma, k)\,\mathrm{cn}^2(\tau, k') + \mathrm{sn}^2(\tau, k') = 0.$$

This condition is equivalent to the two equations

$$\mathrm{sn}\,(\sigma, k)\,\mathrm{cn}\,(\tau, k') = 0,$$
$$\mathrm{sn}\,(\tau, k') = 0.$$

But the second of these, together with (91), implies that $\operatorname{cn}(\tau, k') = \pm 1 \neq 0$. Therefore, the necessary conditions for $\operatorname{sn}(\sigma + i\tau)$ to vanish are

$$\left. \begin{array}{l} \operatorname{sn}(\sigma, \ k) = 0, \\ \operatorname{sn}(\tau, \ k') = 0. \end{array} \right\} \tag{130}$$

Therefore (cf. section 29),

$$\sigma = 2mK(k), \quad \tau = 2nK(k');$$

that is,

$$t = 2mK + 2niK' \tag{131}$$

where m and n are arbitrary integers.

However, formula (99') is not suitable for evaluating $\operatorname{sn}(t, k)$ at these points since, when conditions (130) are satisfied, not only the numerator but also the denominator of the fraction representing $\operatorname{sn}(t, k)$ vanishes. Therefore, let us turn to formula (99). Here, the numerator is equal to zero but the denominator is nonzero [we recall that $\operatorname{cn}(\tau, k') = \pm 1$]. Thus, (131) represents the zeros of $\operatorname{sn}(t, k)$ (all of them).

With the aid of formulas (100') and (100), the reader can show that

$$t = (2m - 1)K + 2niK' \tag{132}$$

provides all the zeros of $\operatorname{cn}(t, k)$, and he can use (101) to show that

$$t = (2m - 1)K + (2n - 1)iK' \tag{133}$$

yields all the zeros of $\operatorname{dn}(t, k)$ (where m and n assume all integral values).

36. With regard to the periodicity of the functions that we are studying, up to now we have considered only their real periods. However, in extending the definition of the functions to the complex plane, imaginary periods can also arise. An example of this kind is the exponential function.

This function e^t as a function of a real variable is not periodic. However, it does have the purely imaginary period $2\pi i$. To see this, let $t = \sigma + \tau i$, where σ and τ are real numbers. Then, from formula (77),

$$e^t = e^{\sigma + i\tau} = e^\sigma (\cos \tau + i \sin \tau).$$

Let us replace t with $t + 2\pi i$. Since $t + 2\pi i = \sigma + (\tau + 2\pi)i$, this is equivalent to replacing τ with $\tau + 2\pi$. We obtain

$$e^{t+2\pi i} = e^{\sigma+(\tau+2\pi)i} = e^\sigma \left[\cos(\tau + 2\pi) + i\sin(\tau + 2\pi)\right] =$$
$$= e^\sigma (\cos\tau + i\sin\tau) = e^t$$

for arbitrary t. From this it follows that $2\pi i$ is a *period* of the function e^t.

Let us recall that a number A is called a period of a function $f(t)$ if the equation

$$f(t + A) = f(t)$$

is satisfied for every t for which the function is defined.

If $f(t)$ has at least one nonzero period, it is said to be a *periodic function*. It follows from the definition that, if A is a period of $f(t)$, then any integral multiple of A is also a period of $f(t)$.

It was shown in section 22 that 2π is a period of the function $\sin t$, treated as a function of a complex variable. Consequently, any integral multiple of 2π is also a period of that function. Let us show that the converse is true: Any period of $\sin t$ is an integral multiple of 2π. Suppose that A is a period of $\sin t$. From the identity

$$\sin(t + A) = \sin t$$

we obtain, for $t = 0$,

$$\sin A = \sin 0 = 0.$$

Consequently, A is zero of the circular sine. According to formula (125), A must be equal to some multiple of π; that is, $A = m\pi$ for some integer m. Let us denote by k the remainder obtained when we divide m by 2. Then, $m = 2p + k$, where p is an integer and k is either zero or 1.

Therefore,

$$\sin(t + A) = \sin(t + k\pi + 2p\pi) = \sin(t + k\pi).$$

The fact that A is a period of $\sin t$ implies that

$$\sin(t + k\pi) = \sin t$$

for arbitrary t. If $k = 0$, this condition is satisfied. If $k = 1$, it cannot be satisfied identically since $\sin(t + \pi) = -\sin t$. Finally, we conclude that $k = 0$, that is, that $A = 2p\pi$, which was what we wished to show.

In an analogous manner, we can show that any period of cos t is an integral multiple of 2π. In summation we may assert that the transition from a real to a complex variable does not bring about any new periods in the study of circular functions.

The situation is different when we study hyperbolic functions. Formulas (52) and (71) provide the quickest path to what we wish to show:

$$\sin(it) = i \sinh t, \qquad \cos(it) = \cosh t,$$

or

$$\sinh(t) = -i \sin(it), \qquad \cosh(t) = \cos(it).$$

From these formulas, we have, for an arbitrary complex number A,

$$\sinh(t + A) = -i \sin(it + iA), \quad \cosh(t + A) = \cos(it + iA).$$

Therefore, A is a period of the hyperbolic functions if and only if iA is a period of the circular functions, that is, if $iA = 2p\pi$, where p is an integer or, in other words, if $A = (-p)2\pi i = 2\pi i p'$, where $p' = 0, \pm 1, \pm 2, \pm 3, \ldots$. Consequently, the hyperbolic functions sinh t and cosh t are periodic functions, and all their periods are given by the formula $A = 2p'\pi i$, where p' is an arbitrary integer.

We see that the transition to a complex variable disclosed the periodicity of the hyperbolic functions (these are not periodic if we consider them as functions of a real variable).

37. Although the periods $2p\pi$ of the circular functions are all real numbers and the periods $2p'\pi i$ of the hyperbolic functions are purely imaginary (except for the period 0), both these classes of functions have in common the fact that any period of the function in question is an integral multiple of some single number. In the case of the circular functions, this number is 2π (or -2π); in the case of the hyperbolic functions, it is $2\pi i$ (or $-2\pi i$). If every period of a periodic function is an integral multiple of some single period, known as the fundamental period, the function is said to be a *singly* periodic function. Thus, the circular and hyperbolic functions are singly periodic functions.

Let us turn to the lemniscate functions, beginning with the lemniscate sine. Noting that $\mathrm{sl}\,\omega = 0$ and

$$\mathrm{cl}\,\omega = \mathrm{sl}\left(\frac{\omega}{2} - \omega\right) = \mathrm{sl}\left(-\frac{\omega}{2}\right) = -\mathrm{sl}\,\frac{\omega}{2} = -1,$$

we obtain the first of expressions (87)

$$\text{sl}\,(t + \omega) = -\,\text{sl}\,t. \tag{134}$$

We see that ω is not a period of $\text{sl}\,t$. From formula (134), it follows that

$$\text{sl}\,(t + 2\omega) = \text{sl}\,[(t + \omega) + \omega] = -\,\text{sl}\,(t + \omega) = \text{sl}\,t. \tag{135}$$

Therefore, 2ω is a period of the lemniscate sine (as we noted in section 25), and hence every integral multiple of 2ω is also a period. However, periods of the form $2n\omega$ do not exhaust all the periods of the lemniscate sine! To see this, let us note that $\text{sl}\,(\omega i) = i\,\text{sl}\,\omega = 0$ and $\text{cl}\,(\omega i) = 1/\text{cl}\,\omega = -1$. If we set $\alpha = t$ and $\beta = i\omega$, in the first of formulas (87), we obtain

$$\text{sl}\,(t + \omega i) = -\,\text{sl}\,t. \tag{136}$$

From this it follows that ωi is not a period of $\text{sl}\,t$. However, we conclude from this same formula (136) that

$$\text{sl}\,(t + 2\omega i) = \text{sl}\,[(t + \omega i) + \omega i] = -\,\text{sl}\,(t + \omega i) = \text{sl}\,t; \tag{137}$$

that is, $2\omega i$, and hence any integral multiple of $2\omega i$, is a period of $\text{sl}\,t$. Thus, the lemniscate sine possesses infinitely many real and infinitely many purely imaginary periods. From this it follows that $\text{sl}\,t$, being a periodic function, is not a singly periodic function. To see this, let us suppose the opposite, namely, that each of its periods is an integral multiple of some nonzero fundamental period α. Then, there must exist nonzero integers m and n such that

$$2\omega = m\alpha, \quad 2\omega i = n\alpha.$$

But this would then imply that $i = n/m$, that is, that i is a real number, which is not the case. Thus, $\text{sl}\,t$ belongs to the special class of periodic functions that are not singly periodic.

By using formulas (134) and (136), we conclude that

$$\text{sl}\,(t + \omega + i\omega) = \text{sl}\,[(t + i\omega) + \omega] = -\,\text{sl}\,(t + i\omega) = \text{sl}\,t.$$

Therefore $\omega + i\omega$ is a periodic of $\text{sl}\,t$, as in any integral multiple of $\omega + i\omega$.

38. From the periods that we have found, we can construct new ones by composition. For example, from the fact that $2\,m\omega$

and $n(\omega + \iota\omega)$ are both periods of $\mathrm{sl}\, t$ (where m and n are both integers), it follows that

$$2m\omega + n(\omega + \omega\iota) \tag{138}$$

is also a period of $\mathrm{sl}\, t$.

Let us show now that every period A of the function $\mathrm{sl}\, t$ can be represented in the form (138) for some integral values of m and n. Of course, for those periods that we have already found, this is obvious:

$$2\omega = 2 \cdot 1 \cdot \omega + 0 \cdot (\omega + \omega\iota), \qquad (m = 1,\ n = 0);$$
$$2\omega\iota = 2 \cdot -1 \cdot \omega + 2 \cdot (\omega + \omega\iota), \qquad (m = -1,\ n = 2);$$
$$\omega + \omega\iota = 2 \cdot 0 \cdot \omega + 1 \cdot (\omega + \omega\iota), \qquad (m = 0,\ n = 1).$$

However, our assertion is of a general character and it states that $\mathrm{sl}\, t$ has no other periods than those that can be represented in the form (138).

Suppose that we have the identity

$$\mathrm{sl}\,(t + A) = \mathrm{sl}\, t \tag{139}$$

Setting $t = 0$ in this identity, we find

$$\mathrm{sl}\, A = 0.$$

From this it follows that A is a zero of the function $\mathrm{sl}\, t$; that is [cf. (128)],

$$A = m\omega + n\omega\iota,$$

where m and n are integers. Let us rewrite A in the form

$$A = (m - n)\omega + n(\omega + \omega\iota) = p\omega + n(\omega + \omega\iota).$$

Let k denote the remainder obtained on dividing p by 2; that is, $p = 2r + k$ (where r is an integer and k is either 0 or 1). Then,

$$A = 2r\omega + n(\omega + \omega\iota) + k\omega.$$

When we substitute this value into (139) and note that $2r\omega + n(\omega + \omega\iota)$ is a period of the form (138), we conclude that

$$\mathrm{sl}\,(t + k\omega) = \mathrm{sl}\, t$$

identically. This condition is satisfied by only one of the two possible values of k, namely, $k = 0$ [that $k = 1$ is impossible is shown by formula (134)].

Thus, any period A of the function $\operatorname{sl} t$ is of the form

$$A = 2r\omega + n(\omega + \omega i),$$

as we wished to show.

The above analysis has brought out the fact that an arbitrary period of $\operatorname{sl} t$ can be represented as a linear combination, with integral coefficients, of the two fundamental periods 2ω and $\omega + \omega i$. Periodic functions possessing such a property are called *doubly periodic*. Thus, $\operatorname{sl}(t)$ is a doubly periodic function with fundamental periods 2ω and $\omega + \omega i$. The reader may verify that we could also have chosen $\omega - \omega i$ and $\omega + \omega i$, for example, as our fundamental periods.

By using the formula

$$\operatorname{cl} t = \operatorname{sl}\left(\frac{\omega}{2} - t\right),$$

the reader can easily derive from what has been shown that $\operatorname{cl} t$ is also a doubly periodic function with the same fundamental periods.

39. An analogous analysis can be made for the Jacobian functions. Let us consider, for example, $\operatorname{sn}(t, k)$. In section 28, it was shown that

$$\operatorname{sn}(t + 2K) = -\operatorname{sn} t,$$

from which it follows that

$$\operatorname{sn}(t + 4K) = \operatorname{sn} t;$$

that is, $4K$ is a real period of $\operatorname{sn} t$. Let us show that $\operatorname{sn} t$ also has imaginary periods. From formula (131), which gives all the zeros of $\operatorname{sn}(t, k)$, we conclude that $t = 2iK'$ is also a zero:

$$\operatorname{sn}(2iK', k) = 0. \tag{140}$$

Furthermore, from formulas (94) and (95), we obtain, for $t = 2K'$,

$$\operatorname{cn}(2iK', k) = \frac{1}{\operatorname{cn}(2K', k')}, \quad \operatorname{dn}(2iK', k) = \frac{\operatorname{dn}(2K', k')}{\operatorname{cn}(2K', k')}. \tag{141}$$

But from formulas (109), it follows that, for $t = 0$,

$$\operatorname{cn}(2K, k) = -\operatorname{cn} 0 = -1, \quad \operatorname{dn}(2K, k) = \operatorname{dn} 0 = 1,$$

or, if we replace k by k' and hence

$$K = \int_0^1 \frac{dt}{\sqrt{(1-t^2)(1-k^2 t^2)}} \quad \text{by} \quad K' = \int_0^1 \frac{dt}{\sqrt{(1-t^2)(1-k'^2 t^2)}}:$$

we have

$$\operatorname{cn}(2K', k') = -1, \quad \operatorname{dn}(2K', k') = 1.$$

Therefore, formulas (141) yield

$$\operatorname{cn}(2iK', k) = -1, \quad \operatorname{dn}(2iK', k') = 1. \tag{142}$$

If we set $\alpha = t$ and $\beta = 2iK'$ in the first of expressions (96) and use formulas (140) and (142), we obtain

$$\operatorname{sn}(t + 2iK', k) = \operatorname{sn}(t, k) \operatorname{cn}(2iK', k) \operatorname{dn}(2iK', k) = \operatorname{sn}(t, k). \tag{143}$$

From this it follows that $2iK'$ is a period of $\operatorname{sn}(t, k)$. From what has been said in the present section, it follows that the complex number

$$A = 4Km + 2iK'n, \tag{144}$$

where m and n are arbitrary integers, is a period of $\operatorname{sn}(t, k)$. Let us show that numbers of the form (144) exhaust all the periods of $\operatorname{sn}(t, k)$. Here, we can reason as in the case of the lemniscate sine (cf. section 37). Let A denote any period of $\operatorname{sn}(t, k)$. Then,

$$\operatorname{sn}(t + A) = \operatorname{sn} t \tag{145}$$

identically. If we set $t = 0$ in (145), we obtain

$$\operatorname{sn} A = 0;$$

that is, A is a zero of the function $\operatorname{sn} t$. Therefore [cf. (131)],

$$A = 2mK + 2iK'n,$$

where m and n are integers. Let r denote the remainder obtained when we divide m by 2:

$$m = 2p + r,$$

where p is an integer and r is either 0 or 1. Then,

$$A = 4pK + 2niK' + 2rK.$$

If we substitute this expression into (145) and note that $4pK + 2niK'$ is a period, we see that

$$\operatorname{sn}(t + 2rK) = \operatorname{sn} t.$$

This relation cannot be satisfied identically if $r = 1$ since $\operatorname{sn}(t + 2K) = -\operatorname{sn} t$. Therefore, $r = 0$, so that

$$A = 4pK + 2niK',$$

which was what we wished to show.

From what we have proven, it follows that $\operatorname{sn}(t, k)$ is a doubly periodic function and we can take $4K$ and $2iK'$ as the fundamental periods. Analogously, one can show that $\operatorname{cn}(t, k)$ is a doubly periodic function with fundamental periods $4K$ and $2K + 2iK'$ [another convenient choice of the fundamental periods of $\operatorname{cn}(t, k)$ are the numbers $2K - 2iK'$ and $2K + 2iK''$] and that the function $\operatorname{dn}(t, k)$ is also a doubly periodic function with fundamental periods $2K$ and $4iK'$.

40. Let us represent on the complex plane all the periods of $\sin t$ and let us draw parallel lines through these points. These lines partition the plane into strips (see Fig. 22), known as *period strips*. Obviously, these strips fill the entire plane without any gaps and without any overlap. The inclination of these lines can be chosen arbitrarily. Let us make the simplest choice and draw them parallel to the imaginary axis. If a point t is allowed to vary in such a way as to assume all values in one of the period strips, the point $t + 2p\pi$ (where p is an integer) will assume all of the values in another period strip. Since $\sin t$ assumes the same values as t and $t + 2p\pi$, all the values assumed by the circular sine in one of these strips are repeated in any other strip. Therefore, for example, when we seek the roots of the equation

$$\sin t = A, \tag{146}$$

where $A = \alpha + i\beta$ (α and β real) is a given complex number, we need only find its roots belonging to any one of these strips. The other roots are obtained from those found by displacements of the form $t' = t + 2p\pi$ (where p is an integer). They occupy in each of the strips the same positions as the original roots do in the original strip.

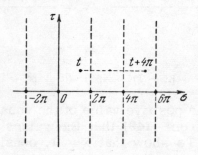

FIG. 22.

Let us show that, for any $A = \alpha + i\beta$, equation (146) has exactly two roots in each period strip. (These two points may merge into a single point, called a *multiple root*.) Here, we need to adopt a convention assigning the boundary line between two strips to one or the other of these strips. Thus, let us assign each such line to the strip lying to the right of it, so that the points of any strip satisfy the inequalities

$$2\pi p \leqslant \sigma < 2\pi(p + 1) \quad (-\infty < \tau < +\infty).$$

For example, the points $t = 0$ and $t = i$ belong to the strip $0 \leqslant \sigma < 2\pi$, and the points 2π and $2\pi + i$ belong to the strip just to the right, namely, the strip $2\pi \leqslant \sigma < 4\pi$. Representing $\sin t$ according to the first of formulas (75), we rewrite equation (146) in the form

$$\sin\sigma \cdot \cosh\tau + i\cos \cdot \sinh\tau = \alpha + i\beta. \qquad (146')$$

We wish to show that there exist only two roots $t = \sigma + i\tau$ satisfying the condition $0 \leqslant \sigma < 2\pi$. Obviously, (146') is equivalent to the system

$$\sin\sigma \cdot \cosh\tau = \alpha, \quad \cos\sigma \cdot \sinh\tau = \beta. \qquad (146'')$$

Let us set $\sin\sigma = x$, $\sinh\tau = y$. Then, these equations take the forms $x\sqrt{1 + y^2} = \alpha$ and $\sqrt{1 - x^2}\,y = \beta$ or

$$x^2 + x^2 y^2 = \alpha^2, \quad y^2 - x^2 y^2 = \beta^2. \tag{147}$$

We are seeking the real solutions of (146″). Therefore, $0 \leqslant x^2 \leqslant 1$ and $0 \leqslant y^2$. These conditions are satisfied only by the values

$$y^2 = \frac{\alpha^2 + \beta^2 - 1 + \sqrt{\Delta}}{2}, \quad x^2 = \frac{\alpha^2 + \beta^2 + 1 - \sqrt{\Delta}}{2}, \tag{148}$$

where

$$\Delta = (\alpha^2 + \beta^2 - 1)^2 + 4\beta^2 = (\alpha^2 + \beta^2 + 1)^2 - 4\alpha^2 \tag{149}$$

and $\sqrt{\Delta}$ denotes the positive value of the square root.

It is obvious from (149) that the values that we have found are nonnegative. To show that $x^2 \leqslant 1$, consider the difference $1 - x^2$:

$$1 - x^2 = \frac{\sqrt{\Delta} - (\alpha^2 + \beta^2 - 1)}{2}.$$

It follows from (149) that this difference is also nonnegative. The equation

$$y^2 - \sinh^2 \tau = \frac{\alpha^2 + \beta^2 - 1 + \sqrt{\Delta}}{2}$$

yields two values of τ that differ only in sign. Corresponding to them are two values of opposite sign, $\sinh \tau$ and $-\sinh \tau$, of the hyperbolic sine but only a single value of the hyperbolic cosine.

The equation

$$x^2 = \sin^2 \sigma = \frac{\alpha^2 + \beta^2 + 1 - \sqrt{\Delta}}{2}.$$

is satisfied by two values of $\sin \sigma$. However, as the first of equations (146″) shows, we should take only the one whose sign is the same as the sign of α (since $\cosh \tau > 1 \geqslant 0$). We denote this value of $\sin \sigma$ (which is the only one possible) by x_0:

$$\sin \sigma = x_0, \quad |x_0| \leqslant 1.$$

Furthermore, corresponding to this value of $\sin \sigma$ are two values of σ in the interval $0 \leqslant \sigma < 2\pi$, which we denote σ_1 and σ_2.

The corresponding values of $\cos \sigma_1$ and $\cos \sigma_2$ differ in sign: $\cos \sigma_1 = - \cos \sigma_2$.

Since the product $\cos \sigma \sinh \tau$ must be equal to β, replacement of σ_1 by σ_2 in the second of equations (146″) must be accompanied with the replacement of one value of τ by its negative $-\tau$. Thus, we have seen that there exist exactly two pairs of values of σ and τ that satisfy (146″) or (146) under the additional condition that $0 \leqslant \sigma < 2\pi$:

$$\sigma_1, \ \tau \text{ and } \sigma_2, \ -\tau.$$

The corresponding points t are

$$t_1 = \sigma_1 + i\tau, \quad t_2 = \sigma_2 - i\tau. \tag{150}$$

Here, σ_1 and σ_2 are determined by the conditions

$$\sin \sigma_j = \pm \sqrt{\frac{\alpha^2 + \beta^2 + 1 - \sqrt{\Delta}}{2}},$$

(for $j = 1, 2$), the sign of $\sin \sigma_j$ coincides with the sign of α, $0 \leqslant \sigma_j < 2\pi$, and $\pm \tau$ is determined by the condition

$$\sinh \tau = \pm \sqrt{\frac{\alpha^2 + \beta^2 - 1 + \sqrt{\Delta}}{2}}.$$

We shall not write out explicit formulas for σ and τ although this would not be difficult.

We note that the points t_1 and t_2 are symmetric about $\pi/2$ if $\alpha > 0$ and that they are symmetric about $3\pi/2$ if $\alpha < 0$.

An analogous analysis could be made for the circular cosine. [The simplest procedure for doing so would be to use the fact that $\cos t = \sin (\pi/2 - t]$.

Let us observe briefly how the results are changed if, instead of the circular sine, we consider the hyperbolic sine. Here, all the periods are purely imaginary, except for 0:

$$0, \ \pm 2\pi i, \ \pm 4\pi i, \ \ldots \ .$$

Therefore, for our period strips, we take strips lying parallel to the real axis (see Fig. 23). The identity

$$\sin (it) = i \sinh t$$

implies that the equation

$$\sinh t = A, \quad t = \sigma + i\tau, \quad 0 < \tau \leqslant 2\pi,$$

is equivalent to the equation

$$\sin(it) = \sin(-\tau + i\sigma) = \sin[(2\pi - \tau) + i\sigma] = iA,$$

where $0 \leqslant \sigma' = 2\pi - \tau < 2\pi$. We have already examined this equation. By using the result obtained for $\sin t$, we see that the equation $\sinh t = A$, for an arbitrary complex number A, has two and only two roots in each of the period strips of the hyperbolic sine. (These roots may merge into a single double root.)

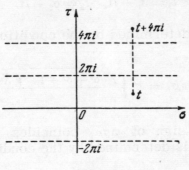

FIG. 23.

41. Let us indicate on the complex plane all the periods of the lemniscate sine:

$$2m\omega + n(\omega + i\omega), \quad m \text{ and } n \text{ integers.}$$

In our studies of the periods of the circular and hyperbolic sines in the preceding section, we partitioned the plane into period strips. Here, we are dealing with a doubly periodic function and, instead of period strips, we naturally have period parallelograms. One of the possible choices of a system of period parallelograms for $\mathrm{sl}\, t$ is shown in Figure 24. As a point t assumes all the values in one of these parallelograms, the point $t + 2m\omega + n(\omega + i\omega)$, where m and n are any fixed integers, assumes all the values in another parallelogram. Since

$$\mathrm{sl}\,[t + 2m\omega + n(\omega + i\omega)] = \mathrm{sl}\, t,$$

the values of $\mathrm{sl}\, t$ assumed in one of the period parallelograms are repeated in every other parallelogram. Therefore, for example, in seeking the roots of the equation

$$\mathrm{sl}\, t = A,\qquad\qquad(151)$$

where $A = \alpha + i\beta$ is a given complex number, we need only find all the roots belonging to any one of these parallelograms, for example, the parallelogram with vertices $0,\ 2\omega,\ 2\omega + (\omega + i\omega)$, and $\omega + i\omega$. All the other roots of equation (151) can be found from these by means of displacements of the form

$$t' = t + 2m\omega + n\,(\omega + i\omega)\,.$$

In each parallelogram, these other roots occupy the same position as do the roots found in the original parallelogram.

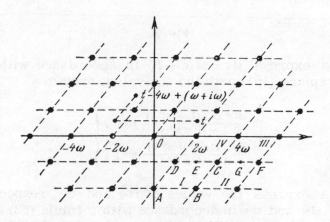

FIG. 24.

Let us show that, for any $A = \alpha + i\beta$, there are two and only two roots in a single parallelogram (these two may merge into a single point, i.e., a double root). Here, we again need to adopt some convention regarding the boundary points that are common to two or more parallelograms. Let us assign to each period parallelogram those points lying on the lower base (other than the right end-point) and the points on the left side (other than the upper end-point).

In the parallelograms I, II, III, and IV shown in Figure 24, for example, the point A belongs to I, the point B to II, the points C and G to III, and the points D and E to IV.

Returning to the theorem mentioned above, let us first prove the following proposition:

The rectangle $0 \leqslant \sigma < 2\omega,\ 0 \leqslant \tau < \omega$ (see Fig. 25) *always contains two and only two roots of equation (151)*.

The original formulation of our assertion will follow from this since the function sl t assumes, by virtue of its periodicity, the same values in the triangle OAB outside the parallelogram $OBEC$, as in the triangle CDE.

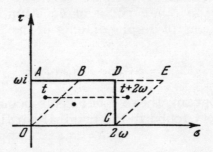

FIG. 25.

Let us express sl $t =$ sl $(\sigma + i\tau)$ in accordance with formula (89) and replace (151) with the equivalent system

$$\left.\begin{array}{c}\dfrac{\text{sl } \sigma \text{ cl } \tau\, (1 + \text{sl}^2\, \tau)}{1 - \text{sl}^2\, \sigma \text{ sl}^2\, \tau} = \alpha, \\[4mm] \dfrac{\text{sl } \tau \text{ cl } \sigma\, (1 + \text{sl}^2\, \sigma)}{1 - \text{sl}^2\, \sigma \text{ sl}^2\, \tau} = \beta. \end{array}\right\} \qquad (152)$$

Let us express the values of cl σ and cl τ, respectively, in terms of sl σ and sl τ in accordance with formula (83) and let us set sl $\sigma = x$ and sl $\tau = y$. Then, the system takes the form

$$\left.\begin{array}{c}\dfrac{x\sqrt{1 - y^4}}{1 - x^2y^2} = \alpha, \\[4mm] \dfrac{y\sqrt{1 - x^4}}{1 - x^2y^2} = \beta. \end{array}\right\} \qquad (152')$$

We are seeking only real solutions of this system that satisfy the conditions $|x| \leqslant 1$ and $0 \leqslant y < 1$ (since sl $\tau \geqslant 0$ for $0 \leqslant \tau < \omega$).

Let us square each of equations (152'), add the result, divide both numerator and denominator of the sum obtained by $1 - x^2y^2$, and then divide the whole equation through by $1 - x^2y^2$. This yields

$$x^2 + y^2 = (\alpha^2 + \beta^2)\,(1 - x^2y^2), \quad \alpha^2y^2\,(1 - x^4) - \beta^2x^2\,(1 - y^4) = 0. \qquad (153)$$

We note that this equation remains unchanged if we simultaneously reverse the roles of x and y on the one hand, and α and β on the other. Eliminating x^2 from (153), we obtain

$$\beta^2 y^8 - [(\alpha^2 + \beta^2)^2 - 1] y^6 - 2 (2\alpha^2 + \beta^2) y^4 +$$
$$+ [(\alpha^2 + \beta^2)^2 - 1] y^2 + \beta^2 = 0. \tag{154}$$

If we divide through by y^4 and make the substitution

$$\frac{1}{y^2} - y^2 = u,$$

we obtain the following quadratic equation for u:

$$\beta^2 u^2 + [(\alpha^2 + \beta^2) - 1] u - 4\alpha^2 = 0. \tag{155}$$

Since the conditions of the problem admit only values of y that are real and do not exceed 1 in absolute value, the quantity $u = 1/y^2 - y^2$ must be a nonnegative number. Therefore, we obtain from (155) the single admissible value of u:

$$u = \frac{\sqrt{[(\alpha^2 + \beta^2)^2 - 1]^2 + 16\alpha^2\beta^2} - [(\alpha^2 + \beta^2)^2 - 1]}{2\beta^2} \geqslant 0. \tag{156}$$

Now, to find y, we have the equation

$$y^4 + u y^2 - 1 = 0. \tag{157}$$

Here again, only one root, a positive one, is possible for y^2. Obviously, this root is less than 2 in absolute value (since the sum of the two possible values of y^2, which is equal to $-u$, is nonpositive). Consequently, it will not exceed unity:

$$0 \leqslant y^2 = \frac{\sqrt{u^2 + 4} - u}{2} \leqslant 1. \tag{158}$$

Since $y = \text{sl}\,\tau \geqslant 0$ (where $0 \leqslant \tau < \omega$), this gives us the only permissible value of y.

Analogously, if we set $1/x^2 - x^2 = v$ and use the symmetry (mentioned above) of the system (153), we obtain

$$v = \frac{\sqrt{[(\alpha^2 + \beta^2)^2 - 1]^2 + 16\alpha^2\beta^2} - [(\alpha^2 + \beta^2)^2 - 1]}{2\alpha^2} \geqslant 0 \tag{159}$$

and hence the only permissible value of x^2:

$$0 \leqslant x^2 = \frac{\sqrt{v^2 + 4} - v}{2} \leqslant 1. \tag{160}$$

From the value that we have found for $y = \text{sl } \tau$:

$$0 \leqslant y = \sqrt{\frac{\sqrt{u^2 - 4} - u}{2}} \leqslant 1$$

we find two values τ_1 and τ_2 of τ in the interval $0 \leqslant \tau < \omega$. These two values are symmetric about $\omega/2$:

$$0 \leqslant \tau_1 = \int\limits_0^y \frac{dt}{\sqrt{1 - t^4}} \leqslant \frac{\omega}{2}, \quad \tau_2 = \omega - \tau_1 \geqslant \frac{\omega}{2}.$$

We note that the corresponding values of $\text{cl } \tau_1$ and $\text{cl } \tau_2$ are negatives of each other (cf. section 5). For definiteness, let us suppose that $y = \text{sl } \tau_1 = \text{sl } \tau_2 > 0$. (We suggest that the reader himself examine the case $y = 0$.) Then, from the second equation in the system (152), it follows that the sign of $\text{cl } \sigma$ coincides with the sign of β. Therefore, for any two possible values σ_1 and σ_1' such that

$$\text{sl } \sigma_1 = \text{sl } \sigma_1' = \sqrt{\frac{\sqrt{v^2 + 4} - v}{2}},$$

where $\sigma_1 \geqslant 0$, $\sigma_1' \geqslant 0$, $\sigma_1 + \sigma_1' = \omega$, we should choose that one (which we assume to be σ_1) such that the signs of $\text{cl } \sigma_1$ and β are the same. Analogously, of the two values σ_2 and σ_2' such that

$$\text{sl } \sigma_2 = \text{sl } \sigma_2' = -\sqrt{\frac{\sqrt{v^2 + 4} - v}{2}},$$

where $\omega \leqslant \sigma_2$, $\omega \leqslant \sigma_2'$ and $\sigma_2 + \sigma_2' = 3\omega$, we choose the one (which we assume to be σ_2) such that the signs of $\text{cl } \sigma_2$ and β are the same.

From what was said in section 5, we can see that $\sigma_1 + \sigma_2 = 2\omega$. (We begin with the fact that $0 \leqslant \sigma_1 \leqslant \omega$, $\omega \leqslant \sigma_2 \leqslant 2\omega$, $\sin \sigma_1 = -\sin \sigma_2$, and $\text{cl } \sigma_1 = \text{cl } \sigma_2$.)

To summarize, we have shown that the system (152) can be satisfied under the conditions $0 \leqslant \sigma < 2\omega$, $0 \leqslant \tau < \omega$ by only two values τ_1 and τ_2 of τ such that

$$\text{sl } \tau_1 = \text{sl } \tau_2 = y > 0, \quad 0 < \text{cl } \tau_1 = -\text{cl } \tau_2 \, (\tau_1 + \tau_2 = \omega),$$

and by two values σ_1 and σ_2 of σ such that

$$\text{sl } \sigma_1 = -\text{sl } \sigma_2 > 0, \quad \text{cl } \sigma_1 = \text{cl } \sigma_2 \quad (\sigma_1 + \sigma_2 = 2\omega),$$

Here, the sign of $\mathrm{cl}\,\sigma_1$ (and that of $\mathrm{cl}\,\sigma_2$) coincides with the sign β.

Since the first equation of the system (152) implies that the sign of $\mathrm{sl}\,\sigma\cdot\mathrm{cl}\,\tau$ coincides with the sign of α, it follows that the signs of $\mathrm{sl}\,\sigma$ and $\mathrm{cl}\,\tau$ must be the same if $\alpha>0$ and opposite if $\alpha<0$). This means that the value σ_1 is compatible with only one of the two values τ_1 and τ_2, namely, with τ_1 in the case $\alpha>0$ and with τ_2 in the case $\alpha>0$. Similarly, the value σ_2 is compatible with τ_2 or with τ_1.

What all this amounts to is that there are two and only two points t_1 and t_2 in the rectangle $0\leqslant\sigma<2\omega$, $0\leqslant\tau<\omega$ that satisfy equation (151). In each of the possible cases, namely,

$$t_1=\sigma_1+i\tau_1, \quad t_2=\sigma_2+i\tau_2=(2\omega-\sigma_1)+i\,(\omega-\tau_1) \quad (\alpha>0),$$
$$t_1=\sigma_1+i\tau_2, \quad t_2=\sigma_2+i\tau_1=(2\omega-\sigma_1)+i\,(\omega-\tau_2) \quad (\alpha<0)$$

the points t_1 and t_2 are symmetric about the center $\omega+i\omega/2$ of the rectangle.

If both these points do not fall simultaneously in the parallelogram $OBEC$, then one of them, let us say, t_1, belongs to the triangle OAB and the other, t_2, belongs to the parallelogram $OBEC$ (Fig. 26). But, in this case, the point $t_1'=t_1+2\omega_1$ falls in $OBEC$, and we again have two roots of equation (151) in that parallelogram. In this case, they are symmetric about the point $2\omega+i\omega/2$.

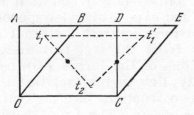

FIG. 26.

42. An analogous analysis could be made for the Jacobian functions with arbitrary modulus. Here, we would need to show that, for arbitrary A, any equation of one of the following forms

$$\mathrm{sn}\,(t,\,k)=A, \quad \mathrm{cn}\,(t,\,k)=A, \quad \mathrm{dn}\,(t,\,k)=A$$

has two and only two roots (which may merge into a single multiple root) in the corresponding period parallelogram. However, the proof would require some tedious calculations, and we shall not go through it.

We prefer to conclude our exposition with a brief survey of the definitions and general properties of elliptic functions. These functions constitute a further generalization of the functions that we have been studying. At the basis of this study is the concept of an entire function of a complex variable.*

A function $f(t)$ of a complex variable is called an *entire function* if it is defined and differentiable at every point of the complex plane. Examples of entire functions are all polynomials, the exponential function (e^t), the circular functions $\sin t$ and $\cos t$, etc. It can be shown that the class of entire functions coincides with the class of functions that can be represented by everywhere-convergent power series:

$$f(t) = a_0 + a_1 t + a_2 t^2 + a_3 t^3 + \ldots + a_n t^n + \ldots$$

A function $\varphi(t)$ of a complex variable is called a meromorphic function (from the Greek words μέροσ "fraction" and μορφή "form") if it can be represented as the quotient of two entire functions:

$$\varphi(t) = \frac{g(t)}{h(t)}.$$

Examples of meromorphic functions are all rational functions (i.e., the quotient of two polynomials), the functions $\sec t = 1/\cos t$, and $\tan t = (\sin t)/\cos t$. It turns out that $\operatorname{sl} t$, $\operatorname{cl} t$, $\operatorname{sn}(t, k)$, $\operatorname{cn}(t, k)$, and $\operatorname{dn}(t, k)$ are also meromorphic functions. However, this assertion requires a special proof and does not follow immediately from the fact that these functions can be expressed by fractions of the forms (89), (90), (99), (100), and (101). The difficulty lies in the fact that the numerators and denominators of these fractions are not entire functions of the complex variable $t = \sigma + i\tau$. The proof that the lemniscate and Jacobian functions can be represented as ratios of entire functions and ways of finding such entire functions are special questions that would take us beyond the scope of the present book. Of course, an entire function $f(t)$ can be regarded as a special case of a meromorphic function since $f(t) = f(t)/1$. However, such a function has a finite value at every value of t without exception, whereas a meromorphic function of the form $\varphi(t) = g(t)/\overline{h(t)}$ has, in general, poles at which it becomes infinite. Obviously, every point $t = t_0$ at which $h(t_0) = 0$ but $g(t_0) \neq 0$ is a pole of the meromorphic function $\varphi(t)$.

---

*See, for example, the author's *Entire Functions*, New York, American Elsevier Publishing Co., 1966.

A meromorphic doubly periodic function is called an *elliptic function* The above implies that the lemniscate and Jacobian functions are elliptic.

One of the basic theorems in the theory of elliptic functions asserts that every nonconstant elliptic function must have at least two poles (which may merge into a single multiple pole) in each of its period parallelograms. From this it follows, in particular, that no nonconstant entire function can be elliptic (that is, doubly periodic).

We shall refer to the number of poles of an elliptic function in its period parallelogram as the *order* of the elliptic function. The Jacobian elliptic functions $\mathrm{sn}\,(t,\,k)$, $\mathrm{cn}\,(t,\,k)$, and $\mathrm{dn}\,(t,\,k)$ (in particular, the lemniscate functions $\mathrm{sl}\,t$ and $\mathrm{cl}\,t$) that we have been studying are second-order functions. The results obtained by performing any of the four rational operations, namely, addition, subtraction, multiplication, and division, on any two elliptic functions with the same fundamental periods $2\omega_1$ and $2\omega_2$ yields another elliptic function with the same periods. In this way, we can obtain functions of arbitrarily high orders. Let $p\,(p \geqslant 2)$ denote the order of a function $f\,(t)$. It can be shown that the equation

$$f\,(t) = A$$

has exactly p roots in any of the period parallelograms of the function f, no matter what the value of the complex number A. (Here, multiple roots are counted in accordance with their multiplicity.)

We see that the theorems on the number of roots of the equations

$$\mathrm{sl}\,t = A, \quad \mathrm{cl}\,t = A, \quad \sin\,(t,\,k) = A, \quad \mathrm{cn}\,(t,\,k) = A, \quad \mathrm{dn}\,(t,\,k) = A$$

in a period parallelogram are special cases of the overall principle.

Without stopping for other properties of elliptic functions, let us point out in conclusion that every elliptic function obeys an algebraic addition theorem. Weierstrass proved a theorem that in a certain sense is the converse of the preceding one: *If a mermomomorphic function $\varphi\,(t)$ possesses an algebraic addition theorem and is not a rational function either of t or of an exponential function of the form $e^{\alpha t}$ (where α is any complex constant), the function φ is necessarily an elliptic function.* (See, for example, the book referred to at the beginning of this section.)

All the general sines that we have been studying obey addition theorems. They are either elliptic functions (as is the case with $\text{sl}\, t$ and $\text{sn}\,(t,\, k)$) or rational functions of an exponential function, as is the case with

$$\sin t = \frac{e^{it} - e^{-it}}{2i},$$

and

$$\sinh t = \frac{e^{t} - e^{-t}}{2}.$$

These facts can be regarded as illustrations of Weierstrass' theorem.

INDEX